A GARLAND OF
MEMORIES

A GARLAND OF
MEMORIES

❋

RUSKIN
BOND

A Garland of Memories

ISBN: 978-81-8158-182-2

Sixth impression 2020
First published 2013

© Ruskin Bond

All rights reserved. No part of this publication may be reproduced or transmitted in any form or by any means, electronic or mechanical, including photocopying, recording, or by any information storage and retrieval system, without permission in writing from the publishers.
Production & layout: Kumar Raman
Printed in India

This edition is distributed exclusively by

Shree Book Centre

8, Kakad Industrial Estate, S. Keer Marg, off L.J. Road
Matunga (west), Mumbai 400 016, India
Tel: +91-22-2437 7516 / 2437 4559 / 2438 0907
Email: sales@shreebookcentre.com
Website: **www.shreebookcentre.com**

Published by
NATRAJ PUBLISHERS
17, Rajpur Road, Dehra Dun 248 001, India
Tel: 0091-135-2654584, 2653382
www.natrajbooks.in

Contents

Acknowledgments

The tales and essays were originally written for various Indian publications—*The Statesman, Times of India, Hindustan Times, Deccan Herald,* among others—and several were first published in the children's magazines, *School* (N.S.W., Australia), *Cricket* (USA), and in *The Christian Science Monitor* (Boston) and *The Lady* (London). The story "The Leopard" first appeared in Blackwood's Magazine (Edinburgh).

Foreword

When I was eight, my father taught me to keep a diary, and although at first it was mostly a record of the films I had seen and the ice-creams and milk-shakes I had consumed, it grew in time to be a little more than that. I began to make observations about the places I'd seen and the friends I'd made, and to describe the changing seasons as reflected in the garden and the countryside.

As I grew older, the diary habit helped me in writing essays and even before I had left school I was writing essays and character sketches for sheer pleasure and not simply as a part of my school work.

At the same time I began to read more widely, and before I was eighteen I had read almost everything written by Dickens, Stevenson, Tagore, Barrie, Maugham, Wodehouse, and several others. Stevenson was a great stylist, a model for the budding essayist; but he could also write a rip-roaring adventure story like *Treasure Island*.

I grew up to be a professional writer, but even while I was making a living from the writing of novels and short stories, I would always be returning to the essay (rather out of fashion in today's world of instant bestsellers) for my own satisfaction and fulfilment.

So over the years I have written many compositions, sketches, vignettes, of which this selection represents about a third. While many of the pieces included here are my personal favourites, I have tried to give the reader a certain variety, so that the subjects range over my childhood world of animals, aunts, uncles and grandparents; the mountains and trees that I have come to love during my long sojourn in the hills; people I have loved or found interesting and unusual; and even the occasional ghost.

These I have Loved

Sea-shells. They are among my earliest memories. I was five years old, walking barefoot along the golden sands of a Kathiawar beach,[1] collecting shells and cowries and taking them home to fill up an old trunk. Some of those shells remained with me through the years, and I still have one. Whenever I put it to my ear, I can listen to the distant music of the Arabian Sea.[2]

A jack-fruit tree. It stood outside my grandfather's house in Dehra Dun: it was easy to climb and generous with its shade; and in its trunk was a large hole where I kept my marbles, sweets, prohibited books, and other treasures.

I have always liked the smell of certain leaves, perhaps even more than the scent of flowers. Crushed geranium and chrysanthemum leaves, mint and myrtle, lime and neem trees after rain, and the leaves of ginger, marigolds and nasturtiums.

Of course there were other smells which, as a boy, I especially liked—the smells of *pillau* and *kofta* curry, hot *jalebis,* roast chicken and fried prawns. But these are smells loved by most gourmets (and most boys), and are not as personal as the smell of leaves and grass.

I have always liked trains and railway-stations. I like eating at railway-stations—hot gram, peanuts, *puris,* oranges... .

As a boy, I travelled to Simla in the little train that crawls round and through the mountains. In March the flowers on the rhododendron trees provided splashes of red against the dark green of the hills. Sometimes there would be snow on the ground to add to the contrast.

What else do I love and remember of the hills? Smells, again... . The smells of fallen pine-needles, cow-dung smoke, spring rain, bruised grass, the pure cold water of mountain streams, the depth and blueness of the sky.

In the hills, I have loved forests. In the plains, I have loved single trees. A lone tree on a wide flat plain—even if it is a thin, crooked, nondescript tree—gains beauty and nobility from its isolation, from the precarious nature of its existence.

Of course I have had my favourites among trees. The banyan, with its great branches spreading to form roots and intricate passageways. The peepul, with its beautiful heart-shaped leaf catching the breeze and fluttering even on the stillest of days. It is always cool under the peepul. The jacaranda and the gulmohar, bursting into blossom with the coming of summer. The cherries, peaches and apricots flowering in the hills; the tall handsome chestnuts and the whispering deodars.

Deodars have often inspired me to poetry. One day I wrote:

> *Trees of God, we call them,*
> *Planted here when the world was young,*
> *The first trees*
> *Their fingers pointing to the stars,*
> *Older than the cedars of Lebanon.*

Several of these trees were cut down recently, and I was furious:

> *They cut them down last spring*
> *With swift efficient tools,*
> *The sap was rising still.*
> *The trees bled,*
> *Slaughtered*
> *To make furniture for fools.*

And which flower is most redolent of India, of the heat and light and colour of India? Not for me the lotus or the water-lily, but the simple marigold, fresh, golden, dew-drenched, kissed by the morning sun.

The smell of the sea... I lived with it for over a year in the Channel Islands.[3] I liked the sea-mist and I liked the fierce gales that swept across the islands in the winter.

Later, there were the fogs of London; I did not like them, but they made me think of Dickens,[4] and I walked to Wapping[5] and the East India Dock Road, and watched the barges on the Thames.[6] I had my favourite pub, and my favourite fish-and-chip shop.

There were always children flying kites from Primrose Hill or sailing boats in the ponds on Hampstead Heath.

Once we visited the gardens at Kew, and in a hothouse, moist and smelling of the Tropics, I remembered the East and some of the simple things I had known—a field of wheat, a stack of sugarcane, a cow at rest and a boy sleeping in the shade of a long red-fingered poinsettia. And I knew I would go home to India.

---

1. A part of the state of Gujarat.
2. The sea between the Indian and the African continents.
3. Group of islands (Part of UK) between France and England.
4. Charles Dickens, 19th Century English novelist.
5. Streets in east end of London.
6. River Thames on the banks of which the city of London is situated.

On Being An Indian

There are many who, given the opportunity to leave India, are only too willing to do so. And yet I, who have had so many opportunities to go away, hang on to Hindustan like a leech.

What is it that keeps me here, while others fly away?

Time and again, I have thought of going away. Sometimes life has been a little rough, and I have thought: I can make a better living in Canada, like my brother; or in Australia, like my cousins; or in England, like some of my friends. But I am not attracted towards these places; their very prosperity frightens me. Not long ago I was offered a well-paid job as a magazine writer in Hong Kong.[1] I thought about it for weeks; worried myself to distraction; and finally, with an enormous sigh of relief, turned it down.

My friends thought I was mad. They still do. Most of them would have jumped at the offer, even if it had meant spending the rest of their lives far from India. Many of my friends do go away and never come back, except perhaps to get married, very quickly, before they are off again. If they do not see a jacaranda tree again, it does not bother them.

But I am terrified at the thought of going away and then being unable to come back. This almost happened to me when, as a boy, I went to England, longed to get back, and did not have the money for the passage. For two years I worked and saved like a miser (something I've never done since) until I had enough for the return passage.

So what is it that keeps me here? My birth? I take too closely after a Nordic grandparent to pass for a typical son of the soil. But India is where I was born and grew up. India is where my father was born and grew to manhood. India is where my grandfather came as a youth.

Surely that entitles me to a place in the Indian sun? If it doesn't, I shall revert to my mother's ancestry and go back to the time of Timur the Lame.

Is it the land itself that holds me? But so many of my fellow-Indians have been born (and reborn) here, and yet they think nothing of leaving the land. They will leave the mountains for the plains; the villages for the cities, the country for another country. And if other lands were a little more willing to open their doors, we would have no population problem—mass emigration would have solved it.

So the land does hold me. But it's more than the land. For India is more than a land. India is an atmosphere. Over thousands of years, the races and religions of the world have commingled here and produced that unique, indefinable phenomenon, the Indian: so terrifying in a crowd, so beautiful in himself.

And oddly enough, I'm one too. I know that I'm as Indian as the postman or the *paanwala* or your favourite MP. Race did not make me one. Religion did not make me one. But history did. And in the long run, it's history that counts.

---

1. An autonomous Chinese island.

A Place of Power

On the first clear day of October, I visited the pine-knoll, my place of peace and power.

It was months since I had last been there. Trips to the plains, a crisis in my affairs, involvements with other people and their troubles, and an entire monsoon, had come between me and the grassy, pine-topped slope facing the eternal snows of the Himalaya. Now I tramped through autumn foliage—tall ferns, sky-blue commelina, wild balsam, purple and orange mushrooms, and bushes festooned with flowering convolvulus—crossed a stream by means of a little bridge of stones, and climbed the steep hill to the pine-knoll.

I felt that when the trees saw me, they made as if to turn in my direction. A puff of wind came across the valley from the distant snows. A long-tailed blue magpie took alarm and flew noisily out of an oak tree. The cicadas were suddenly silent. But yes, the trees remembered me. They bowed gently in the breeze and beckoned me nearer, welcoming me home. Three pines, a straggling oak, and a wild cherry. I went among them, acknowledging their greeting with a touch of my hand against their trunks—the cherry's smooth and polished; the pine's patterned and whorled; the oak's rough, gnarled and full of experience. He has been there the longest, and the wind has beat his upper branches and twisted a few, so that he looks shaggy and undistinguished. But, like the philosopher who is careless about his dress and appearance, the oak has secrets, hidden wisdom. He has been here longer than anyone else and he has learnt the art of survival. In a world where entire forests are being swept away, that is quite an achievement.

While the oak and the pine are much older than me, and have been here since the turn of the century, the cherry tree is exactly ten years old. I know, because I planted it.

One day I had this cherry seed in my hand, and on an impulse I thrust it into the soft earth and then went way and forgot all about it. A few months later I found a tiny cherry tree in the long grass. I did not expect it to survive. But the following year it was two feet tall. And then some goats ate the young leaves and a grasscutter's scythe injured the stem, and I was sure the tree would wither away. But it renewed itself, sprang up even faster. In three years, it was a healthy growing tree, about five feet tall.

I left the hills for a few years—forced by circumstances to make a living in the plains—but this time I did not forget the cherry tree. I thought about it quite often, even sent it telepathic messages of love and encouragement! And when, last year, I returned in the autumn, my heart did a somersault when I found the tree sprinkled with pale pink blossom. (The wild Himalayan cherry flowers in November and not in the spring.)Later, when the fruit was ripe, the tree was visited by finches, tits, bulbuls and other small birds, all coming to feast on the sour red cherries.

In the summer I spent a night on the pine-knoll, sleeping on the grass beneath the cherry tree. I lay awake for hours, listening to the chatter of the stream, the singing of crickets, and the occasional chuckle of some night bird; and watching, through the branches overhead, the stars permanent and impartial in the sky and I felt the power of sky and earth, and the power of a small cherry seed.

And so, when the rains are over, this is where I come, that I might feel the peace and power of this magic place. It's a big world, and momentous events are taking place all the time. But this is where I have seen it all happen.

The River

Between the boy and the river was a mountain. I was a small boy, and it was a small river, but the mountain was big.

The thickly forested mountain hid the river, but I knew it was there and what it looked like; I had never seen the river with my own eyes, but from the villagers I had heard of it, of the fish in its waters, of its rocks and currents and waterfalls, and it only remained for me to touch the water and know it personally.

I stood in front of our house on the hill opposite the mountain, and gazed across the valley, dreaming of the river. I was barefooted; not because I couldn't afford shoes, but because I felt free with, my feet bare, because I liked the feel of warm stones and cool grass, because not wearing shoes saved me the trouble of taking them off.

It was eleven o'clock and I knew my parents wouldn't be home till evening. There was a loaf of bread I could take with me, and on the way I might find some fruit. Here was the chance I had been waiting for: it would not come again for a long time, because it was seldom my father and mother visited friends for the entire day. If I came back before dark, they wouldn't know where I had been.

I went into the house and wrapped the loaf of bread in a newspaper. Then I closed all the doors and windows.

The path to the river dropped steeply into the valley, then rose and went round the big mountain. It was frequently used by the villagers, woodcutters, milkmen, shepherds, mule-drivers—but there were no villages beyond the mountain or near the river.

I passed a woodcutter and asked him how far it was to the river. He was a short, powerful man, with a creased and weathered face, and muscles that stood out in hard lumps.

'Seven miles,' he said, 'Why do you want to know?'

'I am going there,' I said.

'Alone?'

'Of course.'

'It will take you three hours to reach it, and then you have to come back. It will be getting dark, and it is not an easy road.'

'But I'm a good walker,' I said, though I had never walked further than the two miles between our house and my school. I left the woodcutter on the path, and continued down the hill.

It was a dizzy, winding path, and I slipped once or twice and slid into a bush or down a slope of slippery pine-needles. The hill was covered with lush green ferns, the trees were entangled in creepers, and a great wild dahlia would suddenly rear its golden head from the leaves and ferns.

Soon I was in the valley, and the path straightened out and then began to rise. I met a girl who was coming from the opposite direction. She held a long curved knife with which she had been cutting grass, and there were rings in her nose and ears, and her arms were covered with heavy bangles. The bangles made music when she moved her wrists. It was as though her hands spoke a language of their own.

'How far is it to the river?' I asked.

The girl had probably never been to the river, or she may have been thinking of another one, because she said, 'Twenty miles,' without any hesitation.

I laughed and ran down the path. A parrot screeched suddenly, flew low over my head, a flash of blue and green. It took the course of the path, and I followed its dipping flight, running until the path rose and the bird disappeared amongst the trees.

A trickle of water came down the hillside, and I stopped to drink. The water was cold and sharp but very refreshing. But I was soon thirsty again. The sun was striking the side of the hill, and the dusty path became hotter, the stones scorching my feet. I was sure I had covered half the distance: I had been walking for over an hour.

Presently I saw another boy ahead of me, driving a few goats down the path.

'How far is the river?' I asked.

The village boy smiled and said, 'Oh, not far, just round the next hill and straight down.'

Feeling hungry, I unwrapped my loaf of bread and broke it in two, offering one half to the boy. We sat on the hillside and ate in silence.

When we had finished, we walked on together and began talking and talking, I did not notice the smarting of my feet and the heat of the sun and the distance I had covered and the distance I had yet to cover. But after some time my companion had to take another path, and once more I was on my own.

I missed the village boy; I looked up and down the mountain path but no one else was in sight. My own home was hidden from view by the side of the mountain, and there was no sign of the river. I began to feel discouraged. If someone had been with me, I would not have faltered; but alone, I was conscious of my fatigue and isolation.

But I had come more than half way, and I couldn't turn back; I had to see the river. If I failed, I would always be a little ashamed of the experience. So I walked on, along the hot, dusty, stony path, past stone huts and terraced fields, until there were no more fields or huts, only forest and sun and loneliness. There were no men, and no sign of man's influence—only trees and rocks and grass and small flowers—and silence....

The silence was impressive and a little frightening. There was no movement, except for the bending of grass beneath my feet, and the circling of a hawk against the blind blue of the sky.

Then, as I rounded a sharp bend, I heard the sound of water.

I gasped with surprise and happiness, and began to run. I slipped and stumbled, but I kept on running, until I was able to plunge into the snowcold mountain water.

And the water was blue and white and wonderful.

Women of the Snows

Stories of the, Abominable Snowman, or *Yeti,* are common enough. Fully-equipped expeditions have gone out in search of this creature, while so-called *Yeti* scalps have been taken abroad for scientific examination, and famous personalities have clashed over the question of whether the Snowman is myth or reality.

All this fuss about a Snowman would seem to have obscured the fact that there is also an Abominable Snow-woman, as well known to the Nepalese (who call her the *Lidini*) as the *Yeti* is to the Tibetans.

The *Lidini,* like the *Yeti,* is said to be heavy and longhaired. She differs in that her feet are turned in the usual direction and not inward like the *Yeti's.* She has been known to attack on sight, and one can only escape from her by running downhill, because the *Lidini's* progress is slowed down by her huge body, and the long hair that covers her eyes. This should be remembered by anyone setting out in search of the Snow-woman. If you meet her, and try running uphill, she will soon overtake you (she is very fast going uphill), and then you will be at the mercy of her long nails and sharp teeth.

The husband of the *Lidini,* known as the *Banjakhiri,* is said to be gifted with supernatural powers. Waking at dawn, he leaves his forest lair for a large cave in the mountains which he has converted into a shrine. Unlike his wife, he does not attack human beings with intent to kill, but is said to entirely ignore grown-ups, preferring to capture children, whom he hides in his long hair. He takes the children to his cave-shrine, where he looks after them very carefully, feeding them on fruit, rice and earthworms. (The earthworms may be thrown over the shoulder when the *Banjakhiri* isn't looking!)

The *Banjakhiri* has a great school where he teaches children Black Magic. So careful is he in choosing his disciples that only children of the highest intelligence are captured by him. When the youngsters are fully versed in magic, they are taken back to where they were captured, and then sent out into the world to practise their magic on all evil-doers.

There is another couple said to live in the forests of the higher Himalayas: the *Sagpa* and *Sagpani.*

In appearance they resemble the *Banjakhiri* and *Lidini,* but they are much smaller. They, too, attack on sight (though their feet are turned inwards); but beyond the desire to capture living creatures and eat them, their greatest ambition is to sleep as much as possible. You are therefore quite safe if you allow them to sleep undisturbed; but if you wake them, they become very ferocious and do not give you much time in which to start running uphill or downhill. But as a rule the *Sagpanis* avoid human habitation, and are only to be found in the very heart of the great oak and rhododendron forests.

Then there are the *Kasundas*—wild, curly-headed creatures, usually seen at great heights well above the snow-line. Nobody has got close to a *Kasunda*. There is a story that many years ago some Mongol soldiers caught one in Tibet. Finding it to be of an imitative disposition, a soldier gave it a tin containing kerosene oil, while he himself filled a similar tin with water. The soldier poured the water over his own head, and the *Kasunda* immediately imitated his action, pouring the oil over itself. The soldier then took a box of matches, and giving a match to the *Kasunda,* lit one himself and pretended to set fire to his clothes. The *Kasunda* immediately did the same, set his curly hair on fire, and went up in smoke.

Since then, the *Kasundas* have kept well away from human beings. And who can blame them?

Animals on the Track

'ALL ABOARD!' shrieked Popeye, Grandmother's pet parrot, as the family climbed aboard the Lucknow Express. We were moving from Dehra to Lucknow, in Northern India, and as Grandmother had insisted on taking her parrot along, Grandfather and I had insisted on bringing our pets—a teenaged tiger (Grandfather's) and a small squirrel (mine). But we thought it prudent to leave the python behind.

In those days the trains in India were not so crowded and it was possible to travel with a variety of creatures. Grandfather had decided to do things in style by travelling first-class, so we had a four-berth compartment for our own, and Timothy, the tiger, had an entire berth to himself. Later, everyone agreed that Timothy behaved perfectly throughout the journey. Even the guard admitted that he could not have asked for a better passenger: no stealing from vendors, no shouting at coolies, no breaking of railway property, no spitting on the platform.

All the same, the journey was not without incident. Before we reached Lucknow, there was excitement enough for everyone.

To begin with, Popeye objected to vendors and other people poking their hands in at the windows. Before the train had moved out of the Dehra station, he had nipped two fingers and tweaked a ticket-inspector's ear.

No sooner had the train started moving than Chips, my squirrel, emerged from my pocket to examine his surroundings. Before I could stop him, he was out of the compartment door, scurrying along the corridor.

Chips discovered that the train was a squirrel's paradise, almost all the passengers having bought large quantities of roasted peanuts before the train pulled out. He had no difficulty in making friends with both children and grown-ups, and it was an hour before he returned to our compartment, his tummy almost bursting.

'I think I'll go to sleep,' said Grandmother, covering herself with a blanket and stretching out on the berth opposite Timothy's. 'It's been a tiring day.'

'Aren't you going to eat anything?' asked Grandfather.

'I'm not hungry—I had some soup before we left. You two help yourselves from the tiffin-basket.'

Grandmother dozed off, and even Popeye started nodding, lulled to sleep by the clackety-clack of the wheels and the steady puffing of the steam-engine.

'Well, I'm hungry,' I said. 'What did Granny make for us?'

'Ham sandwiches, boiled eggs, a roast chicken, gooseberry pie. It's all in the tiffin-basket under your berth.'

I tugged at the large basket and dragged it into the centre of the compartment. The straps were loosely tied. No sooner had I undone them than the lid flew open, and I let out a gasp of surprise.

In the basket was Grandfather's pet python, curled up contentedly on the remains of our dinner. Grandmother had insisted that we leave the python behind, and Grandfather had let it loose in the garden. Somehow, it had managed to smuggle itself into the tiffin-basket.

'Well, what are you staring at?' asked Grandfather from his corner.

'It's the python.' I said. 'And it's finished all our dinner.'

Grandfather joined me, and together we looked down at what remained of the food. Pythons don't chew, they swallow: outlined along the length of the large snake's sleek body were the distinctive shapes of a chicken, a pie, and six boiled eggs. We couldn't make out the ham sandwiches, but presumably these had been eaten too, because there was no sign of them in the basket. Only a few apples remained. Evidently the python did not care for apples.

Grandfather snapped the basket shut and pushed it back beneath the berth.

'We mustn't let Grandmother see him,' he said. 'She might think we brought him along on purpose.'

'Well, I'm hungry,' I complained.

Just then Chips returned from one of his forays and presented me with a peanut.

'Thanks,' I said. 'If you keep bringing me peanuts all night, I might last until morning.'

But it was not long before I felt sleepy. Grandfather had begun to nod and the only one who was wide awake was the squirrel, still intent on investigating distant compartments.

A little after midnight there was a great clamour at the end of the corridor. Grandfather and I woke up. Timothy growled in his sleep, and Popeye made complaining noises.

Suddenly there were cries of '*Saap, saap!*' (Snake, snake!)

Grandfather was on his feet in a moment. He looked under the berth. The tiffin-basket was empty.

'The python's out,' he said, and dashed out of our compartment in his pyjamas. I was close behind.

About a dozen passengers were bunched together outside the wash-room door.

'Anything wrong?' asked Grandfather casually.

'We can't get into the toilet,' said someone. 'There's a huge snake inside.'

'Let me take a look,' said Grandfather. 'I know all about snakes.'

The passengers made way for him, and he entered the washroom to find the python curled up in the wash-basin. After its heavy meal it had become thirsty and, finding the lid of the tiffin-basket easy to pry up, had set out in search of water.

Grandfather gathered up the sleepy, overfed python and stepped out of the washroom. The passengers hastily made way for them.

'Nothing to worry about,' said Grandfather cheerfully. It's just a harmless young python. He's had his dinner already, so no one is in any danger!' And he marched back to our compartment with the python in his arms. As soon as I was inside, he bolted the door.

Grandmother was sitting up on her berth.

'I knew you'd do something foolish behind my back,' she scolded. 'You told me you'd got rid of that creature, and all the time you've been hiding it from me.'

Grandfather tried to explain that we had nothing to do with it, that the python had smuggled itself into the tiffin-basket, but Grandmother was unconvinced. She declared that Grandfather couldn't live without the creature and that he had deliberately brought it along.

'What will Mabel do when she sees it!' cried Grandmother despairingly.

My Aunt Mabel was a school teacher in Lucknow. She was going to share our new house, and she was terrified of all reptiles, particularly snakes.

'We won't let her see it,' said Grandfather. 'Back it goes into the tiffin-basket.'

Early next morning the train steamed into Lucknow. Aunt Mabel was on the platform to receive us.

Grandfather let all the other passengers get off before he emerged from the compartment with Timothy on a chain. I had Chips in my pocket, suitcases in both hands. Popeye stayed perched on Grandmother's shoulder, eyeing the busy platform with considerable distrust.

Aunt Mabel, a lover of good food, immediately spotted the tiffin-basket, picked it up and said, 'It's not very heavy, I'll carry it out to the taxi. I hope you've kept something for me.'

'A whole chicken,' I said.

'We hardly ate anything,' said Grandfather.

'It's all yours, aunty!' I added.

'Oh, good!' exclaimed Aunt Mabel. 'It's been ages since I tasted something cooked by your grandmother.' And after that there was no getting the basket away from her.

Glancing at it, I thought I saw the lid bulging, but Grandfather had tied it down quite firmly this time, and there was little likelihood of its suddenly bursting open.

An enormous 1950 Chevrolet taxi was waiting outside the station, and the family tumbled into it. Timothy got onto the back seat, leaving enough room for Grand father and me. Aunt Mabel sat up front with Grand mother, the tiffin-basket on her lap.

'I'm dying to see what's inside,' she said, 'Can't I take just a little peep?'

'Not now,' said Grandfather. 'First let's enjoy the breakfast you've got waiting for us.'

'Yes, wait until we get home,' said Grandmother. 'Now tell the taxi driver where to take us, dear. He's looking rather nervous.'

Aunt Mabel gave instructions to the driver and the taxi shot off in a cloud of dust.

'Well, here we go!' said Grandfather. 'I'm looking forward to settling into the new house.'

Popeye, perched proudly on Grandmother's shoulder, kept one suspicious eye on the quivering tiffin-basket.

'All aboard!' he squawked. 'All aboard!'

When we got to our new house, we found a light breakfast waiting for us on the dining table.

'It isn't much,' said Aunt Mabel. 'But we'll supplement it with the contents of your hamper.' And placing the basket on the table, she removed the lid.

The python was half-asleep, with an apple in its mouth. Aunt Mabel was no Eve, to be tempted. She fainted away.

Grandfather promptly picked up the python, took it into the garden, and draped it over a branch of a guava tree.

When Aunt Mabel recovered, she insisted that there was a huge snake in the tiffin basket. We showed her the empty basket.

'You're seeing things,' said Grandfather,

'It must be the heat,' I said.

Grandmother said nothing. But Popeye broke into shrieks of maniacal laughter, and soon everyone, including a slightly hysterical Aunt Mabel, was doubled up with laughter.

What's your Dream?

An old man, a beggar man, bent double, with a flowing white beard and piercing grey eyes, stopped on the road on the other side of the garden wall and looked up at me, where I perched on the branch of a *lichi* tree.

'What's your dream?' he asked.

It was a startling question coming from that raggedy old man on the street: even more startling that it should have been made in English. English-speaking beggars were a rarity in those days.

'What's your dream?' he repeated.

'I don't remember,' I said. I don't think I had a dream last night.'

'That's not what I mean. You know it isn't what I mean. I can see you're a dreamer. It's not the lichi season, but you sit in that tree all afternoon, dreaming.'

'I just like sitting here,' I said. I refused to admit that I was a dreamer. Other boys didn't dream, they had catapults.

'A dream, my boy, is what you want most in life. Isn't there something that you want more than anything else?'

'Yes,' I said promptly. 'A room of my own.'

'Ah! A room of your own, a tree of your own, it's the same thing. Not many people can have their own rooms, you know. Not in a land as crowded as ours.'

'Just a small room.'

'And what kind of room do you live in at present?'

'It's a big room, but I have to share it with my brothers and sisters and even my aunt when she visits.'

'I see. What you really want is freedom. Your own tree, your own room, your own small place in the sun.'

'Yes, that's all.'

'That's all? That's everything. When you have all that, you'll have found your dream.'

'Tell me how to find it!'

'There's no magic formula, my friend. If I was a godman, would I be wasting my time here with you? You must work for your dream, and move towards it all the time, and discard all those things that come in the way of finding it, and then, if you don't expect too much too quickly, you'll find your freedom, your room of your own. The difficult time comes afterwards.'

'Afterwards?'

'Yes, because it's so easy to lose it all, to let someone take it away from you. Or you become greedy, or careless, and start taking everything for granted, and—Poof!—suddenly the dream has gone, vanished!'

'How do you know all this?' I asked.

'Because I had my dream and lost it.'

'Did you lose everything?'

'Yes, just look at me now, my friend. Do I look like a king or a godman? I had everything I wanted, but then I wanted more and more... . You get your room, and then you want a building, and when you have your building, you want your own territory, and when you have your own territory, you want your own kingdom—and all the time it's getting harder to keep everything.

And when you lose it—in the end, all kingdoms are lost—you don't even have your room any more.'

'Did you have a kingdom?'

'Something like that... . Follow your own dream, boy, but don't take other people's dreams, don't stand in anyone's way, don't take from another man his room or his faith or his song.' And he turned and shuffled away, intoning the following verse, which I have never heard elsewhere, so it must have been his own:

> *Live long, my friend, be wise and strong,*
> *But do not take from any man his song.*

I remained in the *lichi* tree, pondering his wisdom and wondering how a man so wise could be so poor. Perhaps he became wise afterwards. Anyway, he was free, and I was free, and I went back to the house and demanded (and got) a room of my own. Freedom, I had begun to realise, was something you had to insist upon.

Uncle Ken and the Zigzag Way

Uncle Ken[1] always maintained that the best way to succeed in life was to zigzag.

'If you keep going off in new directions,' he declared, 'you'll meet with more opportunities!'

Well, opportunities certainly came Uncle Ken's way, but he was not a success in the sense that Dale Carnegie[2] would have defined a successful man...

In a long life devoted to 'muddling through' with the help of the family, Uncle Ken's many projects had included a chicken farm and a mineral water bottling project. For this latter enterprise, he had bought up a thousand old soda-water bottles and filled them with sulphur water from the springs five miles from Dehra. It was good stuff, taken in small quantities. But drunk a bottle at a time, it proved corrosive—'sulphur and brimstone', as one irate customer described it—and angry buyers demonstrated in front of the house, throwing empty bottles over the wall into Grandmother's garden.

Grandmother was furious—more with Uncle Ken than with the demonstrators—and made him give everyone's money back.

'You have to be healthy and strong to take sulphur water,' he explained later.

'I thought it was meant to *make* you healthy and strong,' I said.

Grandfather remarked that it did not compare with plain soda-water, which he took with his whisky. 'Why don't you just bottle soda-water?' he said. 'There's a much bigger demand for it.'

But Uncle Ken believed that he had to be original in all things.

'The secret of success is to zigzag,' he said.

'You certainly zigzagged round the garden when your customers were throwing their bottles back at you,' said Grandmother.

Uncle Ken also invented the zigzag walk.

The only way you could really get to know a place well, he said, was to walk through in a truly haphazard way. To make a zigzag walk, you take the first turning to the left, the first to the right, then the first to the left again and so on. It can be quite fascinating—provided you are in no hurry to reach your destination.

The trouble was, Uncle Ken used this zigzag method even when he had an appointment or a train to catch.

When Grandmother asked him to go to the station to meet Aunt Mabel and her children, who were arriving from Lucknow, he zigzagged through the town, taxing the botanical gardens to the west and the lime-stone factories to the east, finally reaching the station by way of the goods yards, in order, as he said, 'to take it by surprise'.

Nobody was surprised, least of Aunt Mabel, who had taken a *tonga* and reached the house while Uncle Ken was still sitting on the station platform, waiting for the next train to come in. I was sent to fetch him.

'Let's zigzag home again,' he said.

'Only on condition we eat *chaat* every fifteen minutes,' I said.

So we went home by way of all the most winding bazaars (and in north Indian towns they do tend to zigzag) stopping at numerous chaat and *halwai* shops, until Uncle Ken had finished his money. We got home very late and were scolded by everyone; but, as Uncle Ken told me, we were pioneers and had to expect to be misunderstood and even maligned. Posterity would recognise the true value of zigzagging.

'The zigzag way,' he said, 'is the diagonal between heart and reason.'

In our more troubled times, had he taken to preaching on the subject, he might have acquired a large following of drop-outs. But Uncle Ken was the original drop-out. He would not have tolerated any others.

Had he been a space traveller, he would have gone from star to star, zigzagging across the Milky Way.

Uncle Ken may not have succeeded in getting anywhere very fast, but I think he did succeed in getting at least one convert (myself) to see his point: When you zigzag, you are not choosing what you shall see in the world, but are giving the world a chance to see you.

---

1. The author's uncle.
2. The author of *How to Make Friends and Influence People*.

A Year in Jersey

After leaving my school in Simla, I was away from India for three years. As I was frequently homesick and impatient to return, those three years were very long ones for me.

For one of those years I lived in the Channel Islands, on the island of Jersey, which is the largest of the group with an area of 45 square miles. It is nearer to France than it is to Britain. Once a part of Normandy,[1] it was all that remained to Britain of her conquests in France during the Hundred Years' War.

It is perhaps a measure of the unimportance of these islands that no one has ever bothered to fight over them. During World War II, the Germans occupied them without any resistance from Britain. After the War was over, the Germans gave them up with the same absence of fuss.

Jersey's chief source of income is tourism. For those in England who find a trip to the Continent[2] too expensive, the Channel Islands are the next best thing. The summer months are warm and sunny, and the beaches are excellent for bathing. A French *'patois'* is spoken by the original inhabitants—mostly farmers and fisher-men—but when the population doubles itself during the tourist season, English takes over.

I went to Jersey[3] because I had relatives there. I knew no one in England and had no money of my own. It was not long before I discovered that the town of St. Helier (the island's port and capital) gave shelter to a large number of retired Indian Army majors and colonels. They came to Jersey for the sun, and because the income tax wasn't high. The house nameplates on their gates were redolent of old Anglo-India: 'Lucknow Villa', 'Poona Cottage', 'Simla Lodge', to name just a few. These old *koi-hai's* spoke nostalgically of curries, shikar trips, polo, and evenings at the Club.

My year in Jersey was a lonely one. I got on well with the clerks in the office where I worked, but I had no close friends, no one to whom I could talk of books or mountains of India. On summer evenings I would go down to the beach and bathe in the warm salt sea. When the tide was out, I would walk out to some distant rocks, and sit on them for an hour or two, completely cut off from the rest of the world. When there was a storm, I liked to walk along the promenade, watching the waves dash against the rocks and mount the high sea wall.

Having spent my youth in a country like India, which was vast and full of endless variety, I could not get used to living on a small island, the population of which was less than half that of Chandigarh,[4] I took long walks by the sea, dreaming of India, remembering only the good times (and conveniently forgetting the not so good), and making plans to return some day, I had decided to move to London as soon as I had saved some money. I had never before felt so isolated as I had during my year in Jersey and resolved never to live on an island again. It is different in the mountains. You can live on the loneliest mountain-top without feeling lonely. Having the world below yen makes a difference! I learnt that two Indians had lived in Jersey before me. One was a Gujarati student who, finding himself unable to continue his studies in England, had taken a job at the St. Helier[5] docks, helping to unload cargo ships. His work had been rough and strenuous: but he had stuck to it until he had saved enough to pay his passage home to India. Although I had never met him, I admired his determination and decided to follow his example.

The other Indian who had been in Jersey for some time was a Sikh. He was a salesman who had walked all over the island selling cloth. Twenty years ago, very few people in Jersey had seen a Sikh, and he aroused considerable curiosity. But he had not been bothered by the stares, or by the children following him about (much the same thing happens to foreigners in rural India); he had gone about his business, sold his cloth and gone away again.

At the end of a year I had saved £30, which was a decent sum in those days—enough to live on, for about three months; it wouldn't last a week today.

I left my relatives and took the boat to Southampton.[6] In London I felt more at home. A friend made me a well-spiced *korma* curry, and I went to see an extravagant Indian film called *Aan*. Never had Lata Mangeshkar's[7] voice sounded so sweet to my ears!

Strange... London had been only an eight-hour trip from Jersey, and yet I felt whole continents away. In cosmopolitan London, Indians were already much in evidence, and I began to feel a little nearer to home. And I knew it wouldn't be long before I'd be able to return.

---

1. A region of France.
2. Europe.
3. The largest of the Channel Islands.
4. State capital of Punjab and Haryana
5. Port and the capital of Jersey.
6. English seaport.
7. Indian singer and recording artiste.

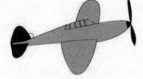

Flattery will get you Everywhere

When I was a boy in Dehra, there was a mango-grove just opposite the bungalow. It belonged to someone called Seth Govind Ram (may his soul rest in peace), and, during the mango season, it was fiercely guarded by a giant of a man called Phambiri. All my efforts to get into the grove were repulsed, and on one occasion I received a mild lathi-blow on my backside.

'I just wanted to climb the tree,' I pleaded.

'Come back when the mango season is over,' said Phambiri with a vicious smile copied from a filmi villain.

And then I discovered that he was an ex-wrestler, that he had been a champion in his youth, and had even thrown the great King Kong.[1] (I did not know at the time that King Kong, in his bad years, was constantly being thrown out of the ring.) So, whenever I passed the grove and saw Phambiri, I would remark on his great strength, his superb condition (going to fat, really), his muscles like cricket balls, and his bull-like neck and shoulders. Gradually he warmed to me, and began to tell me of his exploits. I acclaimed them. Then he showed me feats of strength, like picking up rocks and hurling them across the road. I applauded. Before long, he had invited me into the mango grove, and by the end of the week I could have all the mangoes I wanted. The guardian of the grove actually pressed them upon me.

Flattery will get you everywhere.

One of the first lessons learnt by school children is that the majority of teachers are susceptible to the most blatant forms of flattery. Hard work helps a little, but the child at the top of the class is often held in esteem by teacher as being 'so polite, so sweet, such a little gentleman', etc. This paragon of virtue wears an adoring smile, and always waits till the teacher is out of hearing before slandering her. 'They do but flatter with their lips, and dissemble in their double heart.' The Psalmist was speaking of political hangers-on, but he could have been talking of school children. Their power games are played out on similar lines.

There is of course that cynical old ploy of telling a woman she looks ten years younger than her actual age. This doesn't always work. I once told a woman (who looked fifty) that she looked an attractive forty, and she hit me over the ear with her handbag. It turned out she was thirty.

Be careful when you flatter. The results can sometimes be unexpected.

---

1. A famous wrestler about 40 years ago.

Gentle Shade by Day

Those who have spent some time in non-airconditioned parts of India will remember with gratitude those gracious trees that provide shade and shelter during summer months—the banyan, peepul, mango, neem, and others Coastal dwellers are not so fortunate, for there is not much shade to be had from a palm tree, unless you keep moving with its long but insubstantial shadow.

I am not surprised that the sages of old were given to sitting beneath the peepul tree. They might have had various religious reasons for calling it sacred, but I am sure there was a good practical reason as well. Few trees provide a cooler shade. Even on the stillest of days, the leaf of the peepul is forever twirling; and with thousands of leaves spinning like tops, there is quite a breeze for anyone who rests below.

There are warnings, however, about peepul trees. Gentle shade by day, terror by night! And at night the tree is said to be alive with various spirits, most of them inimical to man. One is advised not to sleep beneath it, for this will be construed by a ghost as an invitation to jump down your throat and take possession of you, or at the very least ruin your digestion.

It is also said to be unlucky to sleep beneath a tamarind, but I have often reclined in the pleasant shade of this noble tree and come to no harm. A famous tamarind stands over the tomb at Gwalior of Tansen, the great singer and musician at Akbar's court. Its leaves, though bitter, are eaten by singers to improve their voices.

A mango grove is a wonderful place for an afternoon siesta. But if the mangoes are ripening, there is usually a good deal of activity going on, with parrots, crows, monkeys and small boys all attempting to evade the watchman who uses an empty kerosene tin as a drum to try and frighten them away. So it's not the ideal place for a nap, but the shade in a mango grove is dark and deep and very soothing.

The banyan tree, with its aerial roots represents the matted hair of God Shiva.[1] There is always shade and space beneath a venerable old banyan. It is still a popular community centre in our Indian villages, but is becoming a rarity in the cities simply because it covers so large an area. And if you cut its aerial roots, the tree topples over. Other handsome trees related to the banyan are the *Pilkhan* and the *Chilkhon,* large spreading evergreens, both quite noticeable on some of New Delhi's wider avenues.

The Neem is a tall tree but its numerous branches give it a shady head. One of my greatest pleasures is to walk beneath an avenue of neem trees after a shower of rain. As the fallen berries are crushed underfoot they give out a sharp, heady fragrance, which I find exhilarating.

Apart from its many medicinal uses, the tree is connected in legend with the Sun God, as in the story of *Neembarak,* 'The Sun in a Neem Tree', who invited to dinner a Bairagi tribal whose rules forbade him to eat except by daylight. When dinner was delayed after sundown, Surajnarayan, the Sun God, obligingly descended from a neem tree and continued shining till dinner was over.

On that pleasant note I end this tribute, only adding that shade-giving trees symbolise the harmony between man and nature, and that our ancestors, in their devotion to trees, and reverence for them, clearly showed that they knew what was good for them.

---

1.   Great Hindu deity.

The Last Days of the Tonga

Tongas, along with tram-cars, haircuts and the Indian rhinoceros, will soon be extinct. In many towns where, ten years ago, there were two or three hundred tongas on the roads, there are now some twenty or thirty. Buses, taxis, above all the ubiquitous scooter-rickshaws, are slowly but surely putting the pony-drawn carriage out of business and out of existence.

This is nowhere more apparent than in Delhi. During World War II, when I was a small boy, the Delhi tonga was the accepted mode of conveyance for high-ranking officers and officials, and for their wives and families. My father and I thought nothing of taking a tonga from Humayun Road to Connaught Place in order to visit a cinema or Davico's[1] restaurant. There was no bus service then, cars were few, the scooter had not been invented, and the only public transport, the tramcar (now obsolete) plied exclusively in Chandni Chowk and environs. In today's Delhi, no one of any standing would think of taking a tonga; it would be *infra dig*. And if a foreign tourist should find a tonga-ride exhilarating, we look on him with the tolerant amusement reserved for eccentrics.

This is all very sad for those who, like this writer, grew up in a tonga-driven world.

When I was very small, I travelled some thirty miles from Dehra Dun to Hardwar in a tonga. There were a few cars about in those days—it was only thirty-five years ago—but a tonga was considered just as good, almost as fast, and certainly more dependable when it came to crossing the Song River—a small tributary of the Ganga.

During the rains, when the river flowed strong and deep, it was impossible to get across except by a hand-operated ropeway (which is still in use in some areas); but during the dry months, when the river was a small stream, the tonga-pony went splashing through, carriage wheels churning through the clear mountain water. If the pony found the going difficult, we removed our shoes, rolled up our trousers, and waded across, while the driver led his pony by the muzzle.

Long before my time, in fact before the turn of the century, when the 'Scinde, Punjab and Delhi Railway' went no further than Saharanpur, the only way of getting to Dehra was by the 'night-mail', better known as the *dak-ghari*.

Dak-ghari ponies were difficult animals, always, attempting to turn around and get into the carriage with the passengers.

It was only when the coach-man used his whip liberally, and reviled the ponies' ancestors as far back as their third and fourth generations, that the beasts could be persuaded to move. And once they started, there was no stopping them; it was a gallop all the way to the first stage, where the ponies were changed to the accompaniment of a bugle blown by the coachman in true Dickensian[2] fashion.

The journey through the Siwaliks really began—as it still does today—at the Mohand[3] Pass. The ascent starts with a gradual gradient, which increases as the road becomes more steep and winding. The hills are abrupt and perpendicular on the southern side, but slope gently away to the north.

At this stage of the journey, drums were beaten (if it was day) and torches were lit (if it was night), because sometimes wild elephants resented the approach of the dakghari and, trumpeting a challenge, would throw the ponies into confusion and panic, and send them racing back to the plains.

There are no wild elephants to be found near Mohand today, and very few other animals. Poachers have seen to that. Tigers, once a fairly common sight, are now almost as rare as dak-gharis.

And now it is the tonga that is nearing extinction. With the emergence of a fairly prosperous middle class in many cities, the machine has taken precedence as a means of conveyance. Trucks, buses, cars, motor-cycles and scooters now ply on routes that were once the monopoly of cycles and tongas. If this can be taken as a measure of a country's progress, then we have certainly forged ahead; but our roads, never meant for such heavy traffic, are frequently cracking up.

Tongas are still to be found, but they are usually confined to roads where buses and taxis do not penetrate. Most tonga-drivers refuse to change with the times, despite a diminishing income. Their ponies seem to have more traffic sense than some of our taxi drivers, and are involved in fewer accidents.

But give a tonga a straight clear stretch of road, and it will go into action, racing at breakneck speed while the passengers cling to their seats for their lives, and the exhilarated driver, shouting his challenge to the machine-age, cracks his whip, calls an endearment to his pony, and bursts into song.

Tonga-drivers vary according to the towns they belong to. In Lucknow they are courteous, garrulous, self-styled descendants of Nawabs.[4] In Delhi they are aggressive, shrewd, matching the temper of the city. Some of them are selling their ponies and buying scooters. Everywhere, tongas are fading away, becoming part of our nostalgia for the past.

---

1. A famous restaurant in the 40s.
2. The coach was the chief mode of travel.
3. Tunnel through the Siwaliks in Dickens' time.
4. Muslim rulers, similar to Hindu Rajas.

Ghosts on the Verandah

Bibiji, my neighbour, a warm attractive woman in her early thirties, is a fount for odd and macabre stories, most of which have their setting in her village near Mathura.

The other night Bibiji launched into an account of the various types of ghosts she had known: the ghosts of immoral women—*churels*—who appeared naked with their feet facing backwards; ghosts with long front teeth, who sucked human blood; and ghosts who take the form of snakes and animals.

One species that I found particularly fascinating was the *munjia* (supposedly the disembodied spirit of a Brahmin youth who died before his marriage) which is said to take up its abode in the branches of a lonely peepul tree. When the spirit is annoyed, it rushes out from the tree and upsets tongas, bullock-carts and bicycles; even a bus is known to have been overturned by a *munjia*. According to Bibiji, should anyone be passing beneath a peepul tree at night, he must be careful not to yawn without covering his mouth or snapping his fingers in front of it. If he doesn't remember to do this, the *munjia* will dash down his throat and completely ruin his digestion.

Among other things, Bibiji told us of the night she had seen the ghost of her husband's first wife. The ghost had lifted Bibiji's baby, then a few months old, out of its cradle, rocked it in her arms for a little while, and announced that she was glad the child was a boy—a sentiment which is not shared by those who know him, for Bibiji's son, now ten, is the most exasperating and dangerous character in the neighbourhood.

The villagers around Mathura (according to Bibiji) have a means by which they can tell what form a departed person takes in his or her next life. After the cremation, some of the loved one's ashes are placed in a basin and left outside at night, covered with a heavy lid. Next morning a footprint is found in the ashes. It may be the footprint of a man or a horse or an elephant according to the form taken by the departed soul. Bibiji told me that one of her more unpleasant aunts left the print of a pig.

In the course of the evening, I mentioned that a friend of mine had found a snake in his bed that very morning. Snakes, declared Bibiji, were very lucky omens if seen early in the morning.

'But what if the snake bites the lucky person.' I asked.

'He will be lucky all the same,' said Bibiji, with a logic that is all her own. She then told us the story of the snake who married a princess.

At first the princess did not agree to marry the snake, whom she had met in a forest, but the snake insisted, saying, 'I will kill you if you don't marry me,' which settled the question. The snake led his bride away and took her to a great treasure. 'I was a prince in my former life,' explained the snake. 'It is all yours.' And then he very gallantly disappeared.

By eleven o'clock I was feeling most reluctant to leave the company on Bibiji's verandah and spend the night alone in my room. I could not help recalling the story of the man who woke in the middle of the night and, putting his hand under the pillow for his watch, touched a mouth, with long teeth and hair all round it. It did not make me feel any better to be told that I should recite certain mantras to keep away the more mischievous spirits. I tried one, which went:

> *Bhut, pret, pisach, dana,*
> *Chhoo mantar, sub nikal jana,*
> *Mano, mano, Shiv ka kahna...*
> *('Ghosts and Spirits assembled here,*
> *Great Shiv is coming. Flee in fear'.)*

But the more I repeated it, the more uneasy I became.

When I got into bed (taking care not to put anything under the pillow), I couldn't lie still, but kept twisting and turning and looking at the walls for suspicious shadows. After sometime I heard knocking at the door, and the voices of my neighbours. Getting up and opening the door, I found Bibiji's daughters looking pale and anxious. In frightening me with their mother's stories, they had also succeeded in frightening themselves.

'Are you all right?' they asked, 'Wouldn't you like to sleep in our house? It might be safer. Come, we'll help you to carry your bed across!'

'I'm quite all right,' I protested; but I was hustled along to the next flat as though a band of ghosts was conspiring against me. Bibiji had been absent during all this activity, and the first we heard of her was a vigorous scream. We ran towards the sound and found her emerging from my room.

'Ruskin's disappeared!' she cried. 'His bed has gone, too!'

And then, when she saw me dashing out of her flat in my pyjamas, she gave another shriek and fainted on the verandah.

Adventures in a Banyan Tree

Though the house and grounds of our home in India were Grandfather's domain, the magnificent old banyan tree was mine—chiefly because Grandfather, at the age of sixty-five, could no longer climb it. (Grandmother used to tease him about this, and would speak of a certain Countess of Desmond,[1] an Englishwoman, who lived to the age of 117, and would have lived longer if she hadn't fallen while climbing an apple tree). The spreading branches of the banyan tree, which curved to the ground and took root again, forming a maze of arches, gave me endless pleasure. The tree was older than the house, older than Grandfather; as old as the town of Dehra, nestling in a valley at the foot of the Himalayas. I could hide myself in its branches, behind thick green leaves, and spy on the world below.

My first friend and familiar was a small grey squirrel. Arching his back and sniffing into the air, he seemed at first to resent my invasion of his privacy. But, when he found that I did not arm myself with a catapult or air gun, he became friendlier. And, when I started leaving him pieces of cake and biscuit, he grew bolder, and finally became familiar enough to take food from my hands.

Before long he was delving into my pockets and helping himself to whatever he could find. He was a very young squirrel, and his friends and relatives probably thought him headstrong and foolish for trusting a human.

In the spring, when the banyan tree was full of small red figs, birds of all kinds would flock into its branches: the red-bottomed bulbul, cheerful and greedy; gossiping rosy pastors; and parrots, and crows, squabbling with each other all the time. During the fig season, the banyan tree was the noisiest place on the road.

Half way up the tree I had built a small platform where I would often spend the afternoons when it wasn't too hot. I could read there, propping myself up against the bole of the tree with cushions taken from the draw-ing room. 'Treasure Island', 'Huck Finn', the 'Mowgli Stories'[2] and the novels of Edgar Wallace, Edgar Rice Burroughs and Louisa May Alcott[3] made up my bag of very mixed reading.

When I didn't want to read, I could look down through the banyan leaves at the world below, at Grandmother hanging up or taking down the washing, at the cook quarrelling with a fruit vendor or at Grandfather grumbling at the hardy Indian marigolds which insisted on springing up all over his very English garden. Usually nothing very exciting happened while I was in the banyan tree, but on one particular afternoon I had enough excitement to last me through the summer.

That was the time I saw a mongoose and a cobra fight to death in the garden, while I sat directly above them in the banyan tree.

It was an April afternoon, and the warm breezes of approaching summer had sent everyone, including Grandfather, indoors. I was feeling drowsy myself and was wondering if I should go to the pond behind the house for a swim, when I saw a huge black cobra gliding out of a clump of cactus and making for some cooler part of the garden. At the same time a mongoose (whom I had often seen) emerged from the bushes and went straight for the cobra.

In a clearing beneath the tree, in bright sunshine, they came face to face.

The cobra knew only too well that the grey mongoose, three feet long, was a superb fighter, clever and aggressive. But the cobra was a skilful and experienced fighter too. He could move swiftly and strike with the speed of light; and the sacks behind his long, sharp fangs were full of deadly venom.

It was to be a battle of champions.

Hissing defiance, his forked tongue darting in and out, the cobra raised three of his six feet off the ground, and spread his broad, spectacled hood. The mongoose bushed his tail. The long hair on his spine stood up. (In the past, the very thickness of his hair had saved him from bites that would have been fatal to others.)

Though the combatants were unaware of my presence in the banyan tree, they soon became aware of the arrival of two other spectators. One was a myna, and the other a jungle crow (not the wily urban crow); they had seen these preparations for battle, and had settled on the cactus to watch the outcome. Had they been content only to watch, all would have been well with both of them.

The cobra stood on the defensive, swaying slowly from side to side, trying to mesmerise the mongoose into making a false move. But the mongoose knew the power of his opponent's glassy, unwinking eyes, and refused to meet them. Instead he fixed his gaze at a point just below the cobra's hood, and opened the attack.

Moving forward quickly until he was just within the cobra's reach, he made a feint to one side. Immediately the cobra struck. His great hood came down so swiftly that I thought nothing could save the mongoose. But the little fellow jumped neatly to one side, and darted in as swiftly as the cobra, biting the snake on the back and darting away again out of reach.

The moment the cobra struck, the crow and the myna hurled themselves at him, only to collide heavily in mid-air. Shrieking at each other, they returned to the cactus plant.

A few drops of blood glistened on the cobra's back.

The cobra struck again and missed. Again the mongoose sprang aside, jumped in and bit. Again the birds dived at the snake, bumped into each other instead, and returned shrieking to the safety of the cactus.

The third round followed the same course as the first but with one dramatic difference. The crow and the myna, still determined to take part in the proceedings, dived at the cobra; but this time they missed each other as well as their mark. The myna flew on and reached its perch, but the crow tried to pull up in mid-air and turn back. In the second that it took him to do this, the cobra whipped his head back and struck with great force, his snout thudding against the crow's body.

I saw the bird flung nearly twenty feet across the garden, where, after fluttering about for a while, it lay still. The myna remained on the cactus plant, and when the snake and the mongoose returned to the fray it very wisely refrained from interfering again!

The cobra was weakening, and the mongoose, walking fearlessly up to it, raised himself on his short legs, and with a lightning snap had the big snake by the snout. The cobra writhed and lashed about in a frightening manner, and even coiled itself about the mongoose, but all to no avail. The little fellow hung grimly on, until the snake had ceased to struggle. He then smelt along its quivering length, and gripping it round the hood, dragged it into the bushes.

The myna dropped cautiously to the ground, hopped about, peered into the bushes from a safe distance, and then, with a shrill cry of congratulation, flew away. When I had also made a cautious descent from the tree and returned to the house, I told Grandfather of the fight I had seen. He was pleased that the mongoose had won. He had encouraged it to live in the garden, to keep away the snakes, and fed it regularly with scraps from the kitchen. He had never tried taming it, because a wild mongoose was more useful than a domesticated one.

From the banyan tree I often saw the mongoose patrolling the four corners of the garden, and once I saw him with an egg in his mouth and knew he had been in the poultry house; but he hadn't harmed the birds, and I knew Grandmother would forgive him for stealing as long as he kept the snakes away from the house.

The banyan tree was also the setting for what we were to call the Strange Case of the Grey Squirrel and the White Rat.

The white rat was Grandfather's—he had bought it from the bazaar for four annas—but I would often take it with me into the banyan tree, where it soon struck up a friendship with one of the squirrels. They would go off together on little excursions among the roots and branches of the old tree.

Then the squirrel started building a nest. At first she tried building it in my pockets, and when I went indoors and changed my clothes I would find straw and grass falling out. Then one day Grandmother's knitting was missing. We hunted for it everywhere but without success.

Next day I saw something glinting in the hole in the banyan tree and, going up to investigate, saw that it was the end of Grandmother's steel knitting-needle. On looking further, I discovered that the hole was crammed with knitting. And amongst the wool were three baby squirrels— all of them white!

Grandfather had never seen white squirrels before, and we gazed at them in wonder. We were puzzled for some time, but when I mentioned the white rat's frequent visits to the trees, Grandfather told me that the rat must be the father. Rats and squirrels were related to each other, he said, and so it was quite possible for them to have offspring—in this case, white squirrels!

---

1. Members of the English aristocracy.
2. Literary classics.
3. Popular novelists.

A Lime Tree in Garhwal

I wake to what sounds like the din of a factory buzzer but is in fact the music of a single vociferous cicada in the lime tree near my bed.

We have slept out of doors, I wake at first light, focus on a pattern of small, glossy leaves, and then through them see the mountains, the mighty Himalayas, striding away into an immensity of sky.

'In a thousand ages of the gods I could not tell thee of the glories of Himachal.' So a poet confessed at the dawn of Indian history, and no one since has been able to do real justice to the Himalaya. We have climbed its highest peaks, but still the mountains remain remote, mysterious, primeval.

No wonder, then, that the people who live on these mountain-slopes, in the mist-filled valleys of Garhwal, have long since learned humility, patience, and a quiet reserve.

I am their guest for a few days. My friend Gajadhar has brought me to his home, to his village above the little Nayar river. We took a train up to the foothills and then we took a bus, and when we were in the hills we walked until we came to this village called Manjari clinging to the terraced slopes of a very proud, very permanent mountain

It is my fourth morning in the village. Other mornings I was woken by the throaty chuckles of the red-billed blue magpies, but today the cicada has drowned all bird song.

Early though it is, I am the last to get up. Gajadhar is exercising in the courtyard. He has a fine physique with the sturdy legs that most hill people possess. I am sure he will realise his ambition of getting into the army. His younger brother Chakradhar, a slim fair youth, is milking the family's buffalo. Their mother is lighting a fire. She is a handsome woman, although her ears, weighed down by heavy silver earrings, have lost their natural shape. The younger children, two small girls, are playing in the courtyard. Their father is in the army, and he is away for most of the year. Gajadhar has been going to a college in the plains; but his mother, with the help of Chakradhar, manages to look after the fields, the house, the goats, and the buffalo. There are spring sowings of corn; monsoon ploughings; September harvestings of rice; and then again autumn sowings of wheat and barley.

They depend on rainfall here, as the village is far above the river. The monsoon is still a month away, but there must be water for cooking, washing and drinking, and this has to be fetched from the river. And so, after a glass each of hot buffalo's milk, the two brothers and I set off down a rough track to the river.

The sun has climbed the mountains but it has yet to reach the narrow valley. We bathe in the river. Gajadhar and Chakradhar dive in off a massive rock; but I wade in circumspectly, unfamiliar with the river's depths and currents. The water, a milky blue, has come from the melting snows and is very cold. I bathe quickly and then dash for a strip of sand where a little sunlight has now spilt down the mountain in warm, golden pools of light.

A little later, buckets filled, we toil up the steep mountainside. A different way this time. We have to take the regular path if we are not to come tumbling down with our pails of water. The path leads up past the school, a small temple, and a single shop in which it is possible to buy soap, salt, and a few other necessities. It is also the post office.

The postman has yet to arrive. The mail is brought in relays from Lansdowne, about thirty miles distant. The Manjari postman, who has to cover eight miles and deliver letters at several small villages on the route, should arrive around noon. He also serves as a newspaper, bringing the village people news of the outside world. Over the years he has acquired a reputation for being highly inventive and sometimes creating his own news; so much so, that when he told the villagers that men had landed on the moon, no one believed him. There are still a few sceptics!

Gajadhar has been walking out of the village almost every day, anxious for a letter. He is expecting the result of his army entrance exam. If he is successful, he will be called for an interview. And then, if he makes a good impression, he will be given training as an officer cadet. After two years he will be a 2nd Lieutenant! His father, after twelve years in the army, is only a corporal. But his father never went to school. There were no schools in the hills in those days.

As we pass the small village school, the children, who have been having a break, crowd round us, eager to have a glimpse of me. They have never seen a stranger. The adults dealt with British officials in the 40s but it is over twenty years since an outsider stepped into the village. I am the cynosure of all eyes. The children exclaim, point at me with delight, chatter among themselves. I might be a visitor from another planet instead of just an itinerant writer from the plains.

For Gajadhar, the day is a trial of his patience,

First we hear that there has been a landslide and that the postman cannot reach us. Then we hear that, although there was a landslide, the postman had already passed the spot in safety. Another alarming rumour has it that the postman disappeared with the landslide. This is soon denied. The postman is safe. It was only the mail bag that disappeared.

And then, at two in the afternoon, the postman turns up. He tells us that there was indeed a landslide but that it took place on someone else's route. A mischievous urchin who passed him on the way was apparently responsible for all the rumours. But we suspect the postman of having something to do with them.

Yes, Gajadhar has passed his exam and will leave with me in the morning. We have to be up early to complete the 30-mile trek in a single day. And so, after an evening with friends, and a folk song from Chakradhar, and a partridge for dinner (a present from a neighbour who thinks Gajadhar will make a fine hus-band for his comely daughter), we retire to our beds: I, to my cot under the lime tree. The moon has not yet risen and the cicadas are silent.

I stretch myself out on the cot under a sky brilliant with stars. And as I close my eyes, someone brushes against the lime tree, bruising its leaves; and the good fresh fragrance of lime comes to me on the night air, making that moment memorable for all time.

Town Birds, Country Birds

Having divided the last ten years of my life between Delhi and Mussoorie, I have come to the heretical conclusion that there is more bird life in the cities than there is in the hills and forests around our hill stations. For birds to survive, they must learn to live with and upon humans; and those birds like crows, sparrows and mynas, who do this to perfection, continue to thrive as our cities grow; whereas the purely wild birds, those who depend upon the forests for life, are rapidly disappearing, simply because the forests are disappearing.

Recently, I saw more birds in one week in a New Delhi colony than I had seen during a month in the hills. In the hills, one must be patient and alert if one is to spot just a few of the birds so beautifully described in Salim Ali's *Indian Hill Birds*. The Babblers and Thrushes are still around, but the Flycatchers and Warblers are seldom seen or heard.

But in Delhi, if you have just a bit of garden and perhaps a guava tree, you will be visited by innumerable bulbuls, tailor-birds, mynas, hoopoes, parrots and tree-pies. Or, if you own an old house, you will have to share it with pigeons and sparrows, perhaps swallows or swifts. And if you have neither garden nor rooftop, you will still be visited by the crows.

Where man goes, the crow follows. He has learnt to perfection the art of living off humans. He will, I am sure, be the first bird on the moon, scavenging among the paper-bags and cartons left behind by untidy astronauts.

Crows favour the densest areas of human population, and there must be at least one for every human. Many crows have obviously been humans in previous lives; they possess all the cunning and sense of self-preservation of the human-being. At the same time, there are many humans who have obviously been crows; we haven't lost their thieving instincts.

Watch a crow sidling along the garden wall with a shabby genteel air, cocking a speculative eye at the kitchen door and any attendant humans. He reminds me of a newspaper reporter, hovering in the background until his chance comes—and then pouncing! I have even known a crow to make off with an egg from the breakfast table. No other bird, except perhaps the sparrow, has been so successful in exploiting human beings.

The myna, although he too is quite at home in the city, is more of a gentleman. He prefers fruit on the tree to scraps from the kitchen, and visits the garden as much out of a sense of sociability as in expectation of hand-outs. He is quite handsome, too, with his bright orange bill and the mask around his eyes. He is equally at home on a railway platform as on the ear of a grazing buffalo, and, being omnivorous, has no trouble in co-existing with Man.

The sparrow, on the other hand, is not a gentleman. Uninvited, he enters your home, followed by his friends, relatives and political hangers-on, and proceeds to quarrel and leave his droppings on the sofa-cushions, with a complete disregard for the presence of humans. The party will then proceed into the garden and destroy all the flower buds. No birds have succeeded so well in making fools of humans.

Although the Bluejay, or Roller, is quite capable of making his living in the forest, he seems to show a preference for the haunts of men, and would rather perch on a telegraph wire than in a tree. Probably he finds the wire a better launching-pad for his sudden rocket flights and aerial acrobatics. In repose he is rather shabby; but in flight when his outspread wings reveal his brilliant blues, he takes one's breath away. As his food consists of beetles and other insect pests, he can be considered a friend and ally.

Parrots make little or no distinction between town and country life. They are the freelances of the bird world—sturdy, independent and noisy. With flashes of blue and green, they swoop across the road, settle for a while in a mango tree, and then, with shrill delighted cries, move on to some other field or orchard. They will sample all the fruit they can, without finishing any. They are destructive birds but, because of their bright plumage, graceful flight and charming ways, are popular favourites and can get away with anything. No one who has enjoyed watching a flock of parrots in swift and carefree flight would want to cage one of these virile birds. Yet so many people do cage them.

After the peacock, perhaps the most popular bird in rural India is the Sarus Crane—a familiar sight around the *jheels* and river banks of northern India and Gujarat. The Sarus pairs for life and is seldom seen without his mate. When one bird dies, the other often pines away and seemingly dies of grief. It is this near-human quality of devotion that has earned the birds this popularity with the villagers of the plains. As a result, they are well protected.

In the long run, it is the 'common man', and not the scientist or conservationist, who can best give protection to the birds and animals living around him. Religious sentiment has helped preserve the peacock and a few other birds. It is a pity that other equally beautiful birds do not enjoy the same protection.

But the wily crow, the cheeky sparrow, and the sensible myna, will always be with us. Quite possibly they will survive even longer than the human species.

And it is the same with other animals. While the cringing jackal has learnt the art of survival, his master the magnificent tiger, is on his way to extinction.

A Face in the Night

It may give you some idea of rural humour if I begin this tale with an anecdote that concerns me.

I was walking alone through an Indian village at night, when I encountered an old man carrying a lantern. I found, to my surprise, that the man was blind.

'If you can't see, why do you carry a lantern?' I asked.

He replied: 'So that fools do not stumble against me in the dark.'

This incident has only a slight relevance to the story that follows, but I think it provides just the right tone.

Some of you may have heard tales rather like the one that follows, and I believe that similar experiences have happened to people in places as far apart as India and Japan. Perhaps it has happened to you. If so, it only goes to show how small the world really is.

Mr. Oliver, an Anglo-Indian teacher, was returning to school late one night, in the hill-station of Simla, in northern India—yes, that same Simla where Kipling's phantom rickshaw plied, and Kim learnt the gentle art of spying. The school he taught in was run on English public school lines, and the boys, most of them Indians from well-to-do families, wore blazers, caps and ties. *Life Magazine,* in a feature on India, had called this school the 'Eton of the East'.

Mr. Oliver had been teaching in the school for several years (he is no longer there, for reasons that will soon become evident). The Simla bazaar, with its cinemas and restaurants, was about two miles distant. Mr. Oliver, a bachelor, usually strolled into town in the evening, returning after dark, when he took a short cut through a pine forest. When there was a strong wind, the pine trees made sad, eerie sounds that kept most people to the main road. But Mr. Oliver was not a nervous or imaginative man. He carried a torch, and on the night I write of, its pale gleam—for the batteries were running down—moved fitfully along the narrow forest path. When its flickering light fell on the figure of a boy, who was sitting alone on a rock, Mr. Oliver stopped in surprise. Boys were not supposed to be out of school after 7 pm and it was now well past nine o'clock.

'What are you doing out here, boy?' asked Mr. Oliver sharply, coming closer in order to recognise the miscreant.

But even as he approached the boy, Mr, Oliver could tell that something was wrong. The boy appeared to be crying. His head hung down, he held his face in his hands, and his body shook convulsively. But it was a strange, soundless weeping, and Mr. Oliver felt distinctly uneasy.

'Well—what's wrong?' asked Mr. Oliver, his anger giving way to concern. 'What are you crying for?'

The boy would not answer or look up. His body continued to be racked with silent sobbing.

'Come on, son, you shouldn't be out here at this hour. Tell me the trouble. Look up!'

The boy did look up. He took his hands from his face and looked up at the teacher. The light from Mr. Oliver's torch fell full on the boy's face—if you could call it a face. There were no eyes, ears, nose or mouth. It was just a round smooth head—with a school-cap on top.

The torch fell from Mr. Oliver's trembling hands. He turned and scrambled down the path, running blindly towards the school and calling for help. He was still running when he saw a lantern swinging in the middle of the path.

Mr. Oliver had never before been so pleased to see the night-watchman. He stumbled up to the watchman, gasping for breath and jabbering incoherently.

'What is it, Sahib?' asked the watchman. 'Has there been an accident? Why are you running?'

'I saw something—something horrible—a boy weeping in the forest—*he had no face!*' 'No face, Sahib!' 'No eyes, no mouth— *nothing!*' 'Do you mean like this, Sahib?' asked the watchman in a matter-of-fact tone, and raised the lamp to his own face.

The watchman had no eyes, no features at all—not even an eyebrow!

As Mr. Oliver screamed, the wind blew the lamp out.

Life's Sweet Sounds

All night the rain has been drumming on the corrugated tin roof. There has been no storm, no thunder, just the steady swish of a tropical downpour. It helps one to lie awake; at the same time, it doesn't keep one from sleeping.

It is a good sound to read by—the rain outside, the quiet within—and, although tin roofs are given to springing unaccountable leaks, there is a feeling of being untouched by, and yet in touch with, the rain.

Gentle rain on a tin roof is one of my favourite sounds. In fact, some of the best sounds are made by water. The water of a mountain stream, always in a hurry, bubbling over rocks and chattering, 'I'm late, I'm late!' like the White Rabbit of *Alice in Wonderland* tumbling over itself in its impatience to reach the bottom of the hill. The sound of the sea, especially when it is far away or when you hear it by putting a seashell to your ear. Then there's the sound made by dried and parched earth as it sucks up a sprinkling of water. Or the sound of water gushing out of the pans of an old well outside a village, while a camel moves silently around the well.

And early in the morning, there are other sounds I like to hear—a crow cawing disconsolately; babblers and bulbuls, bustling in and out of bushes and long grass in search of worms and insects; the sweet, ascending trill of the Himalayan whistling-thrush.

On a cold winter morning in the plains of northern India, if you walk some way into the scrub jungle, you will hear the familiar call of the black partridge: *'Bhagwan Ten Qudrat'* ('Oh God, great is thy might!') it seems to say. The cry rises from the bushes in all directions.

Bells. The jingle of tonga bells. Bells in the hills. A school bell ringing, and children's voices drifting through an open window. A temple bell heard faintly from across the valley. Heavy silver ankle bells on the feet of sturdy hill women. Sheep bells heard high up on the mountain side.

Do falling petals make a sound? Just the tiniest and softest of sounds, like the drift of falling snow. Of course, big flowers, such as dahlias, drop their petals with a very definite plop. These are show-offs, like the hawk-moth who comes flapping into the house at night instead of emulating the butterfly, dipping lazily on the afternoon breeze.

There are sounds that come from a distance, beautiful because they are far away, voices on the wind—'they walketh upon the wings of the wind'. The cries of

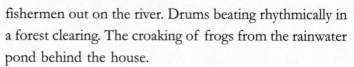

fishermen out on the river. Drums beating rhythmically in a forest clearing. The croaking of frogs from the rainwater pond behind the house.

Homely sounds, though we don't often think about them, are the ones we miss most when they have gone. A kettle on the boil. A door that creaks on its hinges. Old sofa springs. Familiar voices lighting up the dark. Bullock-cart wheels creaking over rough country roads. Ducks quacking in the rain.

And so we return to the rain, with which my favourite sounds began. I have sat out in the open at night, after a shower of rain, when the whole air is murmuring and tinkling with the voices of crickets and grasshoppers and little frogs. There is one melodious sound, a sweet repeated trill, that I have never been able to trace to its source. Perhaps it is a little tree frog, or it may be a small green cricket I shall never know. I am not sure that I really want to know. In an age when a rational explanation has been found for almost everything we see and touch and hear, it is good to be left with one small mystery, a mystery sweet and satisfying and entirely my own.

Another Time and Place

I have often been tempted to revisit the scenes of my childhood—a childhood that I remember as being somewhat idyllic, spent as it was amongst spacious gardens and palaces—but I have refrained from yielding to this temptation, partly because of the disillusionment that lies in wait for anyone who wishes to resurrect the past, and partly because the world I lived in as a child exists no longer, and has already, in the brief period of my youth, passed into history.

At the time I was born, my father had the interesting and rather leisurely job of guardian-tutor to three young Alvar princes; when I was two or three, he held a similar job in Pithadia, one of the Kathiawar States; and by the time I was five, gradually becoming aware of what life was all about, he was guardian-tutor to several young *rajkumars* and *rajkumaris* in the state of Jamnagar.

This was one of the richest states in Kathiawar, with beautiful gardens and palaces. It had a busy little port, where Arab dhows and an occasional steamer would be loading and unloading cargoes of cotton and groundnuts (going out) and coconuts (coming in). There was an airport, too, and a solarium, a sun-hospital with the upper storey revolving on a fixed base. I was six years old when I left Jamnagar, and I have no idea of what the place is like now; but my memories of it are very pleasant. This state probably brought about the popularity of cricket in India, for the great Ranjitsinhji was once its ruler, and Duleepsinhji, who succeeded him as a king of cricket, was his nephew. Jamnagar, in those days, was the Mecca[1] for English touring teams, especially as sumptuous banquets and crocodile-shoots were part of the tourists' itinerary. It was also on the Jamnagar ground that Vinoo Mankad[2] first showed the promise he later so ably fulfilled.

It was, in some ways, a lonely childhood for me. There were hardly any children of my own age to play with, and I wandered about the palace-grounds, looking for adventures in every flower-bed. The cosmos grew to a height of four or five feet, and I accepted it as a good substitute for elephant-grass, and went hunting imaginary tigers with a toy gun.

We did not live in the palace, but in the Tennis Club Bungalow that stood in a corner of the palace-grounds. A high wall surrounded the grounds, and it was in this wall that most of the snakes lived. They were not a menace to us, but all the same one had to be careful. It was not wise to sit down on a chair in the verandah without first taking a look under the cushions. On one occasion a snake had been found curled up under a cushion. We—that is, my father and the cook— had descended upon it with sticks; and panicking, the snake had fled into the bathroom and into the long white marble tub where eventually it was killed. We discovered, later, that it was not a poisonous snake, but nevertheless I refused to bathe again in the marble tub in case I should find another snake in it.

Our Scots terrier, Blackie, was killed by a cobra, but our three tame peacocks were more resilient. They swooped down on any snake that disturbed them, flew with it into the air, and dropped it heavily to the ground. By the time the snake had received several such air-lifts, it would be quite dead. Altogether, life was more perilous for the snakes than it was for us.

Behind the palace was a lake, and beside the lake stood an old deserted palace called Lal Bungalow in which I loved to wander. There was one room, in particular, which exerted a great charm over me. This room had windows on three sides, and each pane of glass was of a different colour. I would take turns looking out on the world—that is, at the lake and the garden—through different coloured glass; at a blue world or a green world or a pink world—I never tired of this fascinating pastime.

A British merchant ship often lay at anchor in the harbour, and as my father was friendly with its Scottish captain—a Captain MacWhirr—we often boarded the ship and had tea with him; that is, I had tea, my father and Captain MacWhirr having a preference for whisky. MacWhirr was a jolly, tobacco-chewing character, who might have come straight out of the pages of Robert Louis Stevenson; but he let me down in a manner that no captain of Stevenson's would have done. He promised to take me with him on his next trip to the Persian Gulf—I failed to notice the wink that must have passed between him and my father—and I spent many blissful hours packing a little attaché case with what I thought I might need on the trip; but the next time I went down to the dock, I found that Captain MacWhirr's ship had gone—it had sailed away the previous day! And I was never able to tell Captain MacWhirr what I thought of him, because we left Jamnagar before his ship came in again.

Others we knew were the Jenkinses, a Welsh couple who ran the state farm, and had a room full of back numbers of *Punch*[3]; Commander Bourne, a retired naval officer, who cut his foot while manicuring his toe-nails with a razor-blade, and, being diabetic, succumbed to a gangrenous infection, (he was a very kind man who gave me bars of chocolate whenever I went to see him); a French cook, who was in charge of all banquets given by His Highness; and the Ghoshes, whose son Buttoo was my first friend, and in whose company I was once chased by a buffalo whilst taking a shortcut across the lake, which was dry during the summer months.

My best friend and ally was my ayah, a strong dark Christian woman who looked after me when my parents were out of station. She introduced me to betel and *supari,* to curried fish, and to all those forbidden sweets that lay tantalisingly in glass cases in the bazaar. Before the ayah came, I had gone through three Anglo-Indian governesses. I was by no means a well-behaved child, and none of the governesses had stayed with us longer than a week; the last one to go complained that I had punched her in the stomach. With my ayah it was different. She possessed a rough, heavy hand, and used it unsparingly on me. And for that I loved her, and love her still.

It was spacious, unhurried living that we knew in those years—a way of life peculiar to that period and now at an end. When we left Jamnagar—in 1939, when my father joined the R.A.F.[4]—we were leaving behind a whole era; for neither my father nor the Indian princely states nor vacancies for 'guardian-tutors' survived into the 1950s.

Appropriately enough, the books I had first learned to read were *Alice in Wonderland* and *Peter Pan*[5] and we did indeed live in a sort of wonderland, a wonderland now difficult to vindicate, but one which remains for me a nostalgic and fond memory of the long summer afternoon that was my childhood.

---

1. The holy place of the Muslims.
2. The famous Indian Cricketer.
3. A magazine.
4. Royal Air Force (Britain).
5. Classic children's story by J.M. Barrie.

The Man Who was King

I was sitting on a bench in London's National Gallery,[1] gazing at a picture of the Madonna and Child[2] when a tall, stooping, elderly gentleman sat down beside me. I gave him a quick glance, noting his swarthy features, the elegant moustache, the horn-rimmed spectacles, before turning politely away. But there was something familiar and disturbing about the face, and I had to look at it again.

When I glanced sideways, I noticed the gentleman was smiling at me.

'Don't you recognise me?' he asked, in a soft, pleasant voice.

'Well, you do seem familiar,' I said: 'Have we met somewhere?'

'Perhaps we have. But if I seem familiar, it is at least something. That's the trouble nowadays. People don't know me any more—I'm a little familiar, that's all. Just a name that stands for a lot of outmoded ideas.'

I was beginning to feel a little perplexed. 'What do you do?' I asked.

'Most of the time I'm remembering,' he said. 'I wrote books once. Poems and stories that set the literary world on fire. Tell me, whose books do you read?'

'Oh, I read a lot of books. Maugham, Hemmingway, Steinbeck, Faulkner? Amongst the older lot, Hardy Bennett,'[4] I hesitated, groping for an important name, and I noticed a shadow, a sad shadow, pass across my companion's face.

'Oh yes, and Kipling,' I said. 'I read a lot of Kipling.'

His face brightened up at once, and the dead eyes behind the thick-lensed spectacles suddenly came to life.

'I'm Kipling,' he said.

I looked at him in astonishment, and then, realising that he might be dangerous, I smiled feebly and said, 'Oh, yes?'

'You probably don't believe me. I'm dead, of course.'

'That's what I always thought.'

'And you don't believe in ghosts?'

'No, I don't.'

'But you'd have no objection to talking to one,' he came along?'

'I'd have no objection. But how do I know you're Kipling's ghost? How do I know you're not a crank?'

'Listen then.'

When my heavens were turned to blood,
When the dark had filled my day,
Furthest, but most faithful, stood

That lone star I cast away.
I had loved myself and I
Have not lived and dare not die.'

'Once,' he said, gripping me by the arm and looking me straight in the eye. 'Once in life I watched a star; but I whistled, "Let her go".'

'Your star hasn't fallen yet,' I said, suddenly moved, suddenly certain that I sat beside Kipling. 'One day, where the spirit of adventure revives, we will discover that there was once a man called Rudyard Kipling.'

'Why have they heaped scorn on me all these years?'

'You were too militant, I suppose; too much of an Empire[5] man. You wrote a lot of patriotic drivel that obscured your finer work.'

He looked a little hurt.

'I am not ashamed of the concept of Empire', he said. 'I was never very political about it. I wrote over six hundred poems, and you could only call about a dozen of them really political. I have been abused for keeping up the theme of the White Man's Burden,[6] but my only aim was to show off the Empire to my audience and I believed the Empire was a fine and noble thing. I never went deeply into political issues. You must remember, my seven years in India were very youthful years. I was in my twenties, a little immature if you like, and my interest in India was a boy's interest. Action appealed to me more than anything else. You must understand that.'

'No one has described action more vividly than you

have. Or India, for that matter. I feel at one with Kim
wherever he goes along the Grand Trunk Road, in the
temples at Benaras, amongst the Saharanpur fruit-gardens,
on the snow-covered Himalayas. *Kim* has colour and
movement and poetry. Only *Huckleberry Finn*[7] is its equal
as an adventure story.'

He sighed, and a wistful look came into his eyes.

'I wish there were more people like you,' said Kipling.

'I'm prejudiced, of course,' I said. 'You see, I've spent
most of my life in India. Not the India of your creation,
but an India that does still have much of the colour and
atmosphere that you caught. You know, Mr. Kipling, you
can still sit in a third-class railway carriage and meet the
most wonderful assortment of people. You can still come
to a village and find the same courtesy, dignity and courage
that the Lama and Kim found on their travels.'

'And the Grand Trunk Road?[8] Is it still a long, winding
procession of humanity?'

'Well, not exactly,' I said, a trifle ruefully. 'It's just a
procession of motor vehicles now. The poor Lama would
be run down by a truck if he became too dreamy on the
Grand Trunk Road. Times *have* changed. There are no more
Mrs. Hauksbees[9] in Simla, for instance.'

There was a far-away look in Kipling's eyes. Perhaps he
was wishing himself a boy again, perhaps he could see the
hills or the red dust of Rajputana; perhaps he was having
a private conversation with Privates Mulvaney and
Otheris,[10] or perhaps he was out hunting with the Seone[11]

wolf-pack. The sound of London's traffic came to us through the glass doors, but we heard only the creaking of bullock-cart wheels and the distant music of a flute.

'Would you look the other way a minute?' he said. 'Look the other way, and count five.'

I did as I was told. When I looked round again, Kipling had gone. I had rather expected that to happen.

I asked the gatekeeper if he had seen a tall man with spectacles and a stoop pass by a few minutes ago.

'Nope,' said the man, scratching his chin. 'Nobody been by for the last ten minutes.'

'Did you see anyone like that go in some time back?'

'Just a couple of American tourists. What did you say this bloke's name was?'

'Kipling,' I said.

'Never heard of him.'

'Didn't you ever read *The Jungle Books*[12]?'

'Sounds familiar. Tarzan[13] stuff, wasn't it?'

'Idiot!' I said, and left him standing on the steps with his mouth hanging open.

The fountains glittered in the sunshine of Trafalgar Square.[14] Children were feeding the pigeons. I wandered about for a long time, but I couldn't find Kipling anywhere.

---

1.   Art museum in London.

2.   The child Christ and mother.

3.   Prominent 20th Century novelists.Bennett,'[1] I hesitated, groping for an important name, and I noticed a shadow, a sad shadow, pass across my companion's face.

4.   Prominent novelists of the early 20th century.

5. The British Empire as it existed before the end of colonial rule.

6. Expression used by Kipling to denote the responsibilities of Empire.

7. Classic American novel by Mark Twain.

8. The main road through northern India.

9. Character in Kipling's Simla stories.

10. Soldiers in Kipling's stories.

11. Jungles in Madhya Pradesh.

12. Kipling's jungle stories feature Mowgli the wolf-boy.

13. Tarzan the ape-man, created by Edgar Rice Burroughs.

14. Centre of London.

Owls in the Family

One winter morning, Grandfather and I found a baby Spotted Owlet by the verandah steps of our home in Dehradun, in northern India. When Grandfather picked it up, the owlet hissed and clacked its bill but then, after a meal of raw meat and water, settled down under my bed.

Spotted Owlets are small birds. A fully grown one is no larger than a thrush and they have none of the sinister appearance of larger owls. I had often found a pair of them in our old mango tree, and by tapping on the tree trunk had persuaded one to show an enquiring face at the entrance to its hole. The owlet is not normally afraid of man nor is it strictly a night bird. But it prefers to stay at home during the day, as it is sometimes attacked by other birds who consider all owls their enemies.

The little owlet was quite happy under my bed. The following day we found a second baby owlet in almost the same spot on the verandah, and only then did we realise that where the rainwater pipe emerged through the roof, there was a rough sort of nest from which the birds had fallen. We took the second young owl to join the first and fed them both.

When I went to bed, they were on the window ledge just inside the mosquito netting, and later in the night their mother found them there. From outside she crooned and gurgled for a long time, and in the morning I found that she had left a mouse with its tail tucked through the netting. Obviously, she put no great trust in me as a foster-parent.

The young birds thrived, and ten days later Grandfather and I took them into the garden to release them. I had placed one on a branch of the mango tree and was stooping to pick up the other when I received a heavy blow on the back of the head. A second or two later the mother owl swooped down at Grandfather, but he was agile enough to duck out of the way.

Quickly, I placed the second owl under the mango tree. Then from a safe distance we watched the mother fly down and lead her offspring into the long grass at the edge of the garden.

We thought she would take her family away from our rather strange household, but next morning I found the two young owlets perched on the hat stand in the verandah.

I ran to tell Grandfather, and when we came back, we found the mother sitting on the birdbath a few metres away. She was evidently feeling sorry for her behaviour the previous day, because she greeted us with a soft 'whoo-whoo'.

'Now there's an unselfish mother for you,' said Grandfather. 'It's obvious she wants us to keep an eye on them. They're probably getting too big for her to manage.'

So the owlets became regular members of our household and were among the few pets that Grandmother took a liking to. She objected to all snakes, most monkeys and some crows—we'd had all of these for pets from time to time—but she took quite a fancy to the owlets and frequently fed them spaghetti.

They seemed to like spaghetti. In fact the owls became so attached to Grandmother that they began to display affection toward anyone in a petticoat, including my Aunt Mabel, who was terrified of them. Aunt Mabel would run screaming from the room every time one of the little birds sidled up to her in a friendly manner.

Forgetful of the fact that Grandfather and I had reared them, the owls would sometimes swell their feathers and peck at anyone in trousers. To avoid displeasing them, Grandfather would often slip into one of Grandmother's petticoats at feeding time. I compromised by wearing an apron and this appeared to satisfy them.

In response to Grandmother's voice the owlets made sounds as gentle and soothing as the purring of a cat, but when wild owls were around, ours would rend the night with blood-curdling shrieks.

They loved to sit and splash in a shallow dish provided

by Grandmother. They enjoyed it even more if cold water was poured over them from a jug while they were in the bath. They would get thoroughly wet, jump out and perch on a towel rack, shake themselves, then return for a second splash and sometimes a third. During the day they dozed on a hat stand. After dark they had the freedom of the house, and their nightly occupation was catching beetles, the kitchen quarters being a happy hunting ground. With their sharp eyes and powerful beaks, they were excellent pest-destroyers.

Looking back on those childhood days, I carry in my mind a picture of Grandmother in her rocking chair with a contented owlet sprawling on her aproned lap. Once, on entering her room while she was taking an afternoon nap, I saw that one of the owlets had crawled up her pillow till its head was snuggled under her ear. Both Grandmother and the little owl were snoring.

The Song of the Whistling-Thrush

I had been in the hills for only a few days when I heard the song of the Himalayan whistling thrush. I did not see the bird that day. It kept to the deep shadows of the ravine below the old stone cottage. I was sitting at the window, gazing out at the new leaves on the walnut and wild pear trees. All was still; the wind was at peace with itself, the mountains brooded massively under a darkening sky. Then, emerging from the depths of the forest like a dark sweet secret came the indescribably beautiful call of the whistling-thrush.

It is a song that never fails to thrill me. The bird starts with a hesitant schoolboy whistle, as though trying out a melody; then, confident of the tune, it bursts into full song, a crescendo of sweet notes and variations that ring clearly across the mountainside. Then suddenly the song breaks off, right in the middle of a cadenza, and the enchanted listener is left wondering what happened to make the bird stop so suddenly. Nothing, really; because a few moments later the song is taken up again.

At first the bird was heard but never seen. Then one day I found the whistling thrush perched on the broken garden fence. He was a glistening deep purple, his shoulders flecked with white; he had sturdy black legs and a strong yellow beak; rather a dapper fellow, who would have looked well in a lop hat, dancing with Fred Astaire. When he saw me coming down the path, he uttered a sharp 'kreeee'— unexpectedly harsh when one remembered his singing— and flew off into the shadowed ravine.

But as the months passed, he grew used to my presence and became less shy. One of my rain-water pipes had blocked, resulting in an overflow of rain water and a small permanent puddle under the stone steps. This became the whistling thrush's favourite bathing-place. On sultry summer afternoons, while I was taking a siesta upstairs, I would hear the bird flapping about in the rain-water pool. A little later, refreshed and sunning himself on the tin roof, he would treat me to a little concert, performed, I cannot help feeling, especially for my benefit.

It was Prakash, the man who brought my milk, who told me the story of the whistling-thrush, or the *Kastura* or *Kaljit*, as the hill men call the bird. According to a legend, the god Krishna fell asleep near a mountain stream, and while he slept, a small boy made off with his famous flute. On waking up and finding his flute gone, Krishna was so angry that he changed the culprit into a bird; but the boy had played on the flute and learnt some of Krishna's wonderful music; and even as a bird he continued, in his disrespectful fashion, to whistle the music of the gods, only stopping now and then (as the whistling-thrush does) when he couldn't remember the right tune.

It wasn't long before the thrush was joined by a female, who was exactly like him. (In fact, I have never been able to tell one from the other.) The pair did not sing together but preferred to give solo performances, waiting for each other to finish before bursting into a song. When, as sometimes happened, they started off together, the effect was not so pleasing to my human ear.

These were love-calls, no doubt, and it wasn't long before the pair were making forays into the rocky ledges of the ravine, looking for a suitable nesting site; but a couple of years were to pass before I saw any of their progeny.

After almost two years in the hills, I came to realise that the thrushes were birds 'for all seasons'. They were liveliest in midsummer; but even in the depths of winter, with snow lying on the ground, they would suddenly start singing, as they flitted from pine to oak to naked chestnut.

As I write, there is a strong wind rushing through the trees and bustling about in the chimney, while distant thunder threatens a summer storm. Undismayed, the whistling-thrushes are calling to each other as they roam the wind-threshed forest. At other times I have heard them clearly above the sound of rushing water. And sometimes they leave the vicinity of the cottage and fly down to the stream, half a mile away, sending me little messages on the wind. Down there, they are busy snapping up snails and insects, the chief items on their menu.

Whistling-thrushes usually nest on rocky ledges, near water; but my overtures of friendship may give my visitors other ideas. Recently, I was away from Mussoorie for about a fortnight. When I returned, I was about to open my window when I noticed a large bundle of ferns, lichen, grass, mud, and moss balanced outside on the window ledge. Peering through the glass, I was able to recognise this untidy basket as a nest. Could such tidy birds make such an untidy nest? Indeed they could, because they arrived and proved their ownership a few minutes later.

Of course that meant I couldn't open the window again. (The nest would have gone over the ledge, if I had.) Fortunately the room has another window, and I kept this one open to let in sunshine, fresh air, and the music of birds and cicadas and the call of the ever welcome postman.

And now, this very day, three pink, freckled eggs lie in the cup of moss that forms the nursery in this jumble of a nest. The parent birds, both male and female, come and go, bustling about very efficiently, fully prepared for the great day that's coming about a fortnight hence.

One small thought occurs to me. The song of one thrush was bright and cheerful. The song of two thrushes was loud and joyful. But won't a choir of *five* whistling-thrushes be a little too much for a solitary writer trying to concentrate at his typewriter? Will I have to make a choice between writing and listening to the birds? Will I one day have to hand the cottage over to the denizens of the forest? Well, we shall have to wait and see. If readers do not hear from me again, they will know whom to blame!

Once you have lived
with Mountains

'In a thousand ages of the gods, I could not tell you of the glories of Himachal.' So wrote a Sanskrit poet who found himself at a loss for words to describe the beauty and magnificence of the Himalayas. But, when you have grown up among these mountains, and go away to live in a distant country, you cannot but try to recapture some of their magic.

It was while I was living in England, in the jostle and drizzle of London, that I remembered the Himalayas at their most vivid.

I had grown up among those great blue and brown mountains; they had nourished my blood; and though I was separated from them by ocean, plain and desert, I could not forget them.

It is always the same with mountains. Once you have lived with them for any length of time, you belong to them. There is no escape.

And so, in London in March, the fog became a mountain mist, and the boom of traffic became the boom of the Ganga emerging from the foothills.

I remembered a little mountain path which led my restless feet into a cool sweet forest of oak and rhododendron and then on to the windswept crest of a naked hilltop. The hill was called Clouds, End.[1] It commanded a view of the plains on one side, and of the snow peaks on the other. Little silver rivers twisted across the valleys below, where the rice fields formed a patchwork of emerald green. And on the hill itself the wind made a *hoo-hoo-hoo* in the branches of the tall deodars where it found itself trapped.

During the rains, clouds enveloped the valley but left the hill alone, an island in the sky. Wild sorrel grew among the rocks, and there were many flowers — convolvulus, clover, wild begonia, dandelion—sprinkling the hill slopes.

On a spur of the hill stood the ruins of an old building. The roof had long since disappeared, and the rain had beaten the stone floors smooth and yellow. Moss and ferns and maidenhair grew from the walls. In a hollow beneath a flight of worn stone steps, a wild cat had made its home. It was a beautiful grey creature, black-striped, with pale green eyes. Sometimes it watched me from the steps or the wall, but it never came near.

No one lives on the hill, except occasionally a charcoal-burner in a temporary grass-thatched hut. But villagers used the path, grazing their sheep and cattle on the grassy slopes. Each cow or sheep had a bell suspended from its neck, to let the shepherd boy know of its whereabouts. The boy could then lie in the sun and eat wild strawberries without the fear of losing his charges.

There was a boy who played a flute. Its rough, sweet, straightforward notes travelled clearly on the mountain air. He would greet me with a nod of his head, without taking the flute from his lips. There was a girl who was nearly always cutting grass for fodder. She wore heavy bangles on her feet, and long silver earrings. She did not speak much either, but she always had a bright smile when she met me on the path. She used to sing to herself, or to the sheep, or to the grass, or to the sickle in her hand.

And there was a boy who carried milk into town (a distance of about five miles), who would often fall into step with me, to hold a long conversation. He had never been away from the hills or in a large city. He had never been in a train. I told him about the cities, and he told me about his village, how they made bread from maize, how fish were to be caught in the mountain streams, how the bears came to steal his father's pumpkins. Whenever the pumpkins were ripe, he told me, the bears would come and carry them off.

These things I remembered—these, and the smell of pine-needles, the silver of oak leaves and the red of maple, the call of the Himalayan cuckoo, and the mist, like a wet face-cloth pressing against the hills.

Odd, how some little incident, some snatch of conversation, comes back to one again, in the most unlikely places. Standing in the aisle of a crowded tube train on a Monday morning, my nose tucked into the back page of someone else's newspaper, I suddenly had a vision of a bear making off with a ripe pumpkin.

A bear and a pumpkin—and there, between Belsize Park and the Tottenham Court Road[2] station, all the smells and sounds of the Himalayas came rushing back to me.

---

1. Name of the estate.
2. Areas in London.

The Man Who Loved Trees

One morning, while I was sitting beside Grandfather on the verandah steps, I noticed the tendril of a creeping vine trailing nearby. As we sat there, in the soft sunshine of a north Indian winter, I saw the tendril moving very slowly towards Grandfather. We gazed at it in fascination. Twenty minutes later, it had crossed the step and was touching his feet.

There is probably a scientific explanation for the plant's behaviour—something to do with light or warmth perhaps—but I liked to think that it moved across the steps simply because it wanted to be near Grandfather. One always felt like drawing close to him. Sometimes when I sat by myself beneath a tree, I would feel rather lonely but as soon as Grandfather joined me, the garden became a happy place. Grandfather had served many years in the Indian Forest Service and it was natural that he would know and like trees. On his retirement, he built a bungalow on the outskirts of the town of Dehradun, planting trees all round: lime, mango, orange and guava; also eucalyptus, jacaranda and the Persian lilac In the fertile Doon Valley, plants and trees grew tall and strong.

There were other trees in the compound before the house was built: including an old peepul that had forced its way through the walls of an abandoned outhouse, knocking the bricks down with its vigorous growth. Peepul trees are great show-offs. Even when there is no breeze, their broad-chested, slim-waisted leaves will spin like tops determined to attract your attention and invite you into their shade.

Grandmother had wanted the peepul tree cut down but Grandfather said, 'Let it be; we can always build another outhouse.'

Grandmother didn't mind trees, but she preferred growing flowers and was constantly ordering seeds and catalogues. Grandfather helped her with the gardening, not because he was crazy about flower gardens but because he liked watching butterflies, and 'there's only one way to attract butterflies,' he said, 'and that's to grow flowers for them.'

Grandfather wasn't content with growing trees in our compound. During the rains, we would walk into the jungle beyond the river-bed, armed with cuttings and saplings, which we would plant in the forest.

'But no one ever comes here!' I protested, the first time we did this. 'Who's going to see them?'

'We're not planting them simply to improve the view,' replied Grandfather. 'We're planting for the forest and for the birds and animals who live here and need more food and shelter.'

'Of course men need trees too,' he added. 'For keeping the desert away; for attracting rain; for preventing the banks of rivers from being washed away; for fruit and flower, leaf and seed. Yes, and for timber too. But men are cutting down the trees without replacing them. And if we don't plant a few ourselves, there'll come a time when the world will be one great desert.'

The thought of a world without trees became a sort of nightmare to me, and I helped Grandfather in his tree-planting with greater enthusiasm. And while we went about our work, he taught me a poem by George Morris:

Woodman, spare that tree!
Touch not a single bough!
In youth it sheltered me,
And I'll protect it now.

'One day the trees will move again,' said Grandfather. 'They've been standing for thousands of years, but there was a time when they could walk about like people. Then along came an interfering busybody who cast a spell over them, rooting them to one place. But they're always trying to move. See how they reach out with their arms! And some of them, like the banyan tree with its travelling aerial roots, manage to get quite far!'

We found an island, a small rocky island in a dry riverbed. It was one of those riverbeds, so common in the foothills, which are completely dry in summer but flooded during the monsoon rains. A small mango tree was growing on the island. 'If a mango can grow here,' said Grandfather, 'so can other trees.'

As soon as the rains set in, and while the river could still be crossed, we set out with a number of tamarind, laburnum and coral-tree saplings and cuttings, and spent the day planting them on the island.

The monsoon season was the time for rambling about. At every turn there was something new to see. Out of earth and rock and leafless bough, the magic touch of the rains had brought life and greenness. You could see the broad-leaved vines growing. Plants sprang up in the most unlikely places; a peepul would take root in the ceiling, a mango would sprout on the window-sill. We did not like to remove them, but they had to go if the house was to be kept from falling down.

'If you want to live in a tree, it's all right by me,' said Grandmother crossly. 'But I like having a roof over my own head, and I'm not going to have my roof brought down by the jungle.'

When the Second World War came, I was sent away to a boarding school and during the holidays I went to live with my father in Delhi. Meanwhile, my grandparents sold the house and went to England. Two or three years later I, too, went to England and I was away from India for several years.

Recently, however, I was in Dehradun again. After first visiting the old house—it hadn't changed much—I walked out of town towards the riverbed. It was February. As I looked across the dry watercourse, my eye was immediately caught by the spectacular red plumes of the coral blossom. In contrast with the dry riverbed, the island was a small green paradise. When I went up to the trees, I noticed that some squirrels were living in them, and a *koel—a* crow-pheasant—challenged me with a mellow 'who-are-you, who-are-you.'

But the trees seemed to know me; they whispered among themselves and beckoned me nearer. And looking around, I noticed that other smaller trees and wild plants and grasses had sprung up under their protection.

Yes, the trees we had planted long ago had multiplied. They were *walking* again. In one small corner of the world, Grandfather's dream had come true.

Bears of the Himalayas

Most Himalayan villages lie in the valleys, where there are streams, tolerably fertile soil, and protection from the biting winds that come through the mountain passes in winter. The houses are usually made of rough granite, and have sloping slate roofs that enable the heavy monsoon rain to run off easily. During the dry autumn months, the roofs are often covered with pumpkins, left there to ripen in the sun.

One October night, when I was sleeping in a friend's house in a village in Garhwal, I was woken by a rumbling and thumping on the roof. I woke my friend and asked him what was happening.

'It's only a bear,' he said.

'Is it trying to get in?' I asked.

'No—it's after the pumpkins.'

A little later we looked out of the small window and saw a black bear making off through a field, like a thief in the night, with a pumpkin held to his chest.

In winter, when snow covers the higher mountains, the brown and black Himalayan bears descend to lower altitudes in search of food. Sometimes they forage in fields. Because they are short-sighted, and suspicious of anything that moves, they can be dangerous; but, like most wild animals, they will avoid men if they can, and are aggressive only when accompanied by their cubs.

Hill people are always advising me to run downhill if chased by a bear. They say that bears find it easier to run uphill than downhill.

Himalayan bears like pumpkins, maize, plums and apricots and, of course, honey. Once, while I was sitting in an oak tree, hoping to see a pair of pine-martens who lived nearby, I heard the whining grumble of a bear, and presently saw one amble into the clearing near the tree.

At first he put his nose to the ground and sniffed his way along until he came to a large anthill. Here he began huffing and puffing, blowing rapidly in and out of his nostrils, so that the dust from the anthill flew in all directions. But he was a disappointed bear, because the anthill had been deserted long before. And so, grumbling, he made his way to a wild plum tree and, shinning rapidly up the smooth trunk, was soon perched in the topmost branches. It was only then that he saw me.

He at once scrambled several feet higher up the tree and laid himself out flat on a branch. It wasn't a very thick branch and left a large expanse of the bear showing on either side. He tucked his head away behind another branch and, so long as he could not, see me, was satisfied that he was well hidden, though he couldn't help grumbling with anxiety.

But, like all bears, he was full of curiosity. And slowly, inch by inch, his black snout appeared over the edge of the branch. As soon as his eyes came into view and met mine, he drew his head back with a jerk and hid his face.

He did this several times. I waited until he wasn't looking, then moved some way down the tree. When he looked up again and saw that I was missing, he was so pleased that he stretched right across to another branch and helped himself to a plum. My burst of laughter so startled him that he tumbled out of the tree, dropped through the branches for some 15 feet, and landed with a thud in a heap of dry leaves. He was quite unhurt but ran from the clearing, grunting and squealing with fright.

The inquisitiveness of bears was revealed to me on another occasion when, hearing that one had been active in a field of maize, I sat up for it at night in the company of one of my friends. We took up our position on a high promontory of rock which gave us a clear view of the moonlit field. A little after midnight a bear came down to the edge of the field, but he was suspicious and probably smelt that men had been about the place recently. He was, however, hungry; so, after standing up as high as possible on his hind legs and peering about to see if the field was empty, he came cautiously out of the forest and made his way toward the ripe corn.

About halfway there his attention was suddenly taken by some Buddhist prayer-flags which had been strung up between two small trees. (They had probably been placed there by Tibetans, some of whom had settled not far away.) On spotting the flags, the bear gave a little grunt of disapproval and began to get back into the forest; but the fluttering was a puzzle he felt he had to make out, so after a few backward steps he again stopped and watched them.

Not satisfied with this, he stood on his hind legs looking at the flags, first at one side and then at the other. Still unsatisfied, he advanced until he was a few yards away from them, again got on his hind legs and examined them from various points of view. Then, seeing that they did not attack him and did not appear dangerous, he approached warily, taking only two or three steps at a time, and having a good look each time before again advancing. Eventually he went confidently up to the flags and pulled them all down. After examining them carefully, he moved on into the field of corn.

But my friend (whose field it was) decided that he wasn't going to lose any more of his crop, so he started shouting, and the villagers woke up and came out of their houses beating drums and empty kerosene tins.

Deprived of his dinner, the bear made off in a bad temper. He ran downhill, and at a good speed too, and I was glad I wasn't in his path just then. Uphill or downhill, an angry bear is best given a very wide berth.

A Long Story

I live on the top of a hill, and my grandson's school is at the bottom of the hill, so I thought it would be a good idea if I walked the two miles to school with him every morning. It would be company for him; and it ought to do wonders for my sagging waistline.

'Tell me a story,' he said, the first time we set off together.

And so I told him one. And the next day I told him another. A story a day, told on the long walk through the deodars, became routine. Until I discovered that in this way I was writing myself out—that, story invented and told, I would come home to the realisation that the day's creative work was done and that I couldn't face my desk or typewriter,

So I decided it had to be a serial story. And I found that the best way to keep it going was to invent a man-eating leopard who carried off a different victim every day. An expanding population, I felt, could sustain his depredations over the months and even the years.

Small boys love bloodthirsty man-eaters, and my grandson was no exception. Every day, in the story, one of the townsfolk disappeared, a victim to the leopard's craving for human flesh. He started with the town gossip and worked his way through the clerk who'd lost my file, the barber who'd cut my hair too short, and the vendor who'd sold me last year's fireworks, and—well, there's no end to the people who can be visualised as suitable victims. I must confess that I was getting as much pleasure out of the tale as my godson: I think Freud would have had something to say about my attitude.

'When is it going to be shot?' asked Rakesh one day.

'Not yet,' I said, 'not yet'.

But towards the end of the year I was beginning to have qualms of conscience. Who was I, a mere mortal, to decide who should be eaten and who should survive? Although the population had been reduced, the accommodation problem remained the same.

Well, things came to a head when a real leopard appeared on the hillside and made off with my neighbour's pet Pekinese.

Had I, with my fevered imaginings, brought into being an actual leopard? Only a dog-eater, true; but one never knew when it might start on people. And I was still well fleshed, in spite of the long walks.

So the story had to end.

'The man-eater is dead,' I announced the other day.

'Who shot it?'

'It wasn't shot. It just died.'

'Of old age?'

'No. Of ulcerative colitis.'

'What's that?' asked my grandson.

'Acute indigestion,' I said.

Goldfish Don't Bark

I'll say this for goldfish: they don't bark.

After several years of living with a nervous Peke who barks at shadows and bites postmen, it's nice to have the sort of pet that doesn't bark, talk, screech, chatter or growl. In these days of ever-increasing noise, the silence of goldfish is indeed golden. Better still, they don't mess the carpet.

I've had my goldfish for three years, and they have never spoken a word in either anger or reproach. I like it that way. I am content to stand and watch them gliding and twisting in a liquid silence, their mouths opening and closing without ever emitting a sound—at least, none that I can hear.

There are four of them in the tank. The oldest and largest has lost a lot of his colour (in the same way that we lose our hair, I suppose). Perhaps this is due to age; or perhaps it's a sort of fishy leucoderma.

Goldfish is a misnomer. Mine are a bright orange. They do acquire a golden tinge when the early morning sun comes through the window and slants across the glass of the tank.

Otherwise they are flowers of fire, waving about in the cool blue of their watery home.

Unlike other aquarium fish, goldfish don't need a lot of fuss and attention, which is another reason why I like them. Their water need be changed only once a month (the less it's changed, the better), and for food, a few bread-crumbs are sufficient. They do very well on a simple diet. Underfeeding won't harm them, whereas overfeeding will certainly kill them off.

Last winter I had to go away for a couple of months, and I had to leave the goldfish behind. There was no one to feed them. When I returned, I expected to find them dead. The water was rather murky, but the fish were alive and well. They did not even seem happy to see me.

Whenever I feel restless, I sit down and watch the goldfish. They never fail to calm my nerves. There they are spending their entire lives in a few cubic feet of water without apparently suffering from any form of neuroses. Their very aimlessness appeals to me. They eat, they come up for the occasional breath of air, and I suppose they sleep, although I have never seen them at it.

Perhaps they sleep while swimming. Most of the time they are swimming around in circles. It is consoling to know that no matter how aimless our human existence may seem to be, we cannot rival goldfish when it comes to being busy doing nothing for a long time.

The Leopard

I first saw the leopard when I was crossing the small stream at the bottom of the hill. The ravine was so deep that for most of the day it remained in shadow. This encouraged many birds and animals to emerge from cover during the hours of daylight. Few people ever passed that way; only milkmen and charcoal-burners from the surrounding villages. As a result, the ravine had become a little haven of wildlife, one of the few natural sanctuaries left near Mussoorie.

Below my cottage was a forest of oak and maple and Himalayan rhododendron. A narrow path twisted its way down through the trees, over an open ridge where red sorrel grew wild, and then down steeply through a tangle of wild raspberries, creeping vines and the slender rangal-bamboo. At the bottom of the hill, the path led on to a grassy verge, surrounded by wild dog-roses. It is surprising how closely the flora of the lower Himalaya, between 5,000 to 8,000 feet, resembles that of the English countryside. The streams ran close by the verge, tumbling over smooth pebbles, over rocks worn yellow with age, on its way to the plains and to the little Song river and finally to the sacred Ganga.[1]

When I first discovered the stream, it was early April and the wild roses were flowering, small white blossoms lying in clusters. There were still yellow and blue primroses on the hill-slopes, saxifrage growing in the rocks, and an occasional late-flowering rhododendron providing a splash of crimson against the dark green of the hill.

I walked down to the stream almost every day, after I had done two or three hours of writing. I had lived in the cities far too long, and had returned to the hills to renew myself, physically and mentally, to get rid of some of the surplus flesh that had gathered about my waist, and, if possible, to write a novel.

Nearly every morning, and sometimes during the day, I heard the cry of the barking deer. And in the evening, walking through the forest, I disturbed parties of kaleej-pheasant. The birds went gliding down the ravine on open, motionless wings. I saw pine-martens and a handsome red fox; I recognised the footprints of a bear.

As I had not come to take anything from the jungle, the birds and animals soon 'grew accustomed to my face', as Mr. Higgins[2] would have said. Or possibly they recognised my footsteps. After some time, my approach did not disturb them. A Spotted Forktail, which at first used to fly away, now remained perched on a boulder in the middle of the stream while I got across by means of other boulders only a few yards away. The Forktail's plumage blended with the rocks and running water, so that the bird was difficult to spot at a distance, but the white 'Cross of St. Andrew'[3] across its back eventually gave it away. Its tail moved gently up and down, in a slow, elegant movement, and its sharp, creaky call followed me up the hillside.

The *langurs* in the oak and rhododendron trees, who would at first go leaping through the branches at my approach, now watched me with some curiosity as they munched the tender green shoots of the oak. The young ones scuffled and wrestled like boys, while their parents groomed each other's coats, stretching themselves out on the sunlit hillside—beautiful animals with slim waists and long, sinewy legs and tails full of character. But one evening, as I passed, I heard them chattering in the trees, and I was not the cause of their excitement.

As I crossed the stream and began climbing the hill, the grunting and chattering increased, as though the langurs were trying to warn me of some hidden danger. A shower of pebbles came rattling down the steep hillside, and I looked up to see a sinewy orange-gold leopard poised on a rock about twenty feet above me.

It was not looking towards me, but had its head thrust attentively forward in the direction of the ravine. But it must have sensed my presence, because slowly it turned its head and looked down at me. It seemed a little puzzled at my presence there; and when, to give myself courage, I clapped my hands sharply, the leopard sprang away into the thickets, making absolutely no sound as it melted into the shadows.

I had disturbed the animal in its quest for food. But a little later I heard the quickening cry of a barking deer as it fled through the forest; the hunt was still on.

The leopard, like other members of the cat family, is nearing extinction in India, and I was surprised to find one so close to Mussoorie. Probably the deforestation that had been taking place in the surrounding hills had driven the deer into this green valley; and the leopard, naturally, had followed.

It was some weeks before I saw the leopard again, although I was often made aware of its presence. A dry, rasping cough sometimes gave it away. At times I felt almost certain that I was being followed. And once, when I was late getting home, and the brief twilight gave way to a dark, moonless night, I was startled by a family of porcupines running about in a clearing. I looked around nervously and saw two bright eyes staring at me from a thicket. I stood still, my heart banging away against my ribs. Then the eyes danced away, and I realised that they were only fireflies.

In May and June, when the hills were brown and dry, it was always cool and green near the stream, where ferns and maidenhair and long grasses continued to thrive.

Downstream I found a small pool where I could bathe, and a cave with water dripping from the roof, the water spangled gold and silver in the shafts of sunlight that pushed through the slits in the cave roof. 'He maketh me to lie down in green pastures; he leadeth me beside still waters.' Perhaps David had discovered a similar paradise when he wrote those words; perhaps I too would write good words. The hill-station's summer visitors had not discovered this haven of wild and green things, I was beginning to feel that the place belonged to me, that dominion was mine.

The stream had at least one other regular visitor, the Spotted Forktail, and though it did not fly away at my approach, it became restless if I stayed too long, and then it would move from boulder to boulder uttering a long complaining cry. I spent an afternoon trying to discover the bird's nest, which I was certain contained her young, because I had seen the parent bird carrying grubs in her bill. The problem was that when the bird flew upstream I had difficulty in following her rapidly enough, as the rocks were sharp and slippery. Eventually I decorated myself with bracken fronds, and, slowly making my way upstream, hid myself in the hollow stump of a tree, at a spot where the Forktail often disappeared. I had no wish to rob the bird of its young; I was simply curious to see its home.

By crouching down, I was able to command a view of a small stretch of the stream and the sides of the ravine; but I had done little to deceive the Forktail, who continued to object strongly to my presence so near her home. I summoned up my reserves of patience, and sat perfectly still for about ten minutes, when the Forktail quietened down. Out of sight, out of mind! But where had *she* gone? Probably into the walls of the ravine where, I felt sure, she was guarding her nest. So I decided on trying to take her by surprise, and jumped up like a jack-in-the-box, in time to see—not the Forktail on her doorstep, but the leopard, bounding away with a grunt of surprise! Two urgent springs and it had crossed the stream and plunged into the forest.

Needless to say, I was as astonished as the leopard, and forgot all about the Forktail and her nest. Had the leopard been following me again? I decided against this possibility. Only man-eaters follow humans, and, so far as I knew, there had never been a man-eater in the vicinity of Mussoorie.

During the monsoon the stream became a rushing torrent, bushes and small trees were swept away, and the friendly murmur of the water became a threatening boom. I did not visit the place too often, as there were leeches in the long grass. But it was always worthwhile tramping through the forest to feast my eyes on the foliage that sprang up in tropical profusion—soft, spongy moss; great stag-ferns on the trunks of trees; mysterious-looking lilies and orchids; wild dahlias, and the climbing convolvulus opening its purple secrets to the morning sun.

One day I found the remains of a barking deer which had been partially eaten. I wondered why the leopard had not hidden the remains of his meal, and decided that it must have been disturbed while eating. Then, climbing the hill, I met a party of shikaris resting beneath the oaks. They asked me if I had seen leopard. I said I had not. They said they knew there was a leopard in the forest. Leopard-skins, they told me, were selling in Delhi at over a thousand rupees each! Of course there was a ban on the export of skins, but they gave me to understand that there were ways and means . . . I thanked them for their information and walked on, feeling uneasy and disturbed.

The shikaris had seen the carcass of the deer, and they had seen the leopard's pug-marks, and they kept coming to the forest. Almost every evening I heard their guns banging away; for they were ready to fire at almost anything.

'There's a leopard about,' they always told me 'You should carry a gun.'

'I don't have one,' I said.

There were fewer birds to be seen, and even the langurs had moved on. The red fox did not show itself; and the pine-martens, who had become quite bold, now dashed into hiding at my approach. The smell of one human is like the smell of any other.

And then the rains were over and it was October and I could lie in the sun, on sweet-smelling grass, and gaze up through a pattern of oak leaves into a blinding-blue heaven. And I would praise God for leaves and grass and the smell of things, the smell of mint and bruised clover, and the touch of things, the touch of grass and air and sky, the touch of the sky's blueness.

I thought no more of the men. I had seen them as the species *Homo Sapiens*,[4] and not as individual personalities. My attitude to them was similar to the attitude of the denizens of the forest. They were men, unpredictable, and to be avoided if possible.

On the other side of the ravine rose Pari Tibba, Hill of the Fairies, a bleak, scrub-covered hill, where no one lived. It was said that in the previous century Englishmen had tried building their houses on the hill, but that the area had always attracted lightning, due either to the hill's situation or to its mineral deposits; and that, after several houses had been struck by lightning, the settlers had moved on to the next hill, where the hill station now stands. To the hill men it is Pari Tibba, haunted by the spirits of a pair of ill-fated lovers who perished there in a storm; to others it is known as Burnt Hill, because of its scarred and stunted trees.

One day, after crossing the stream, I climbed Pari Tibba—a stiff undertaking, because there was no path to the top and I had to scramble up a precipitous rock-face with the help of rocks and roots that were apt to come away in my groping hand. But at the top was a plateau with a few pine trees, their upper branches catching the wind and humming softly. There I found the ruins of what must have been the houses of the first settlers—just a few piles of rubble, now overgrown with weeds, sorrel, dandelions and nettles.

As I walked through the roofless ruins, I was struck by the silence that surrounded me, the absence of birds and animals, the sense of complete desolation. The silence was so absolute that it seemed to be shouting in my ears. But there was something else of which I was becoming increasingly aware: the strong feline odour of one of the cat family.

I paused and looked about. I was alone. There was no movement of dry leaf or loose stone. The ruins were for the most part open to the sky. Their rotting rafters had collapsed, and joined together to form a low passage like the entrance to a mine; and this dark cavern seemed to lead down into the ground.

The smell was stronger when I approached this spot, so I stopped again and waited there, wondering if I had discovered the lair of the leopard, wondering if the animal was now at rest after a night's hunt. Perhaps it crouched there in the dark, watching me, recognising me, knowing me as the man who walked alone in the forest without a weapon. I like to think that he was there, that he knew me, and that he acknowledged my visit in the friendliest way: by ignoring me altogether.

Perhaps I had made him confident—too confident, too careless, too trusting of the human in his midst. I did not venture any further; I was not out of my mind. I did not seek physical contact, or even another glimpse of that beautiful sinewy body, springing from rock to rock. It was his trust I wanted, and I think he gave it to me.

But did the leopard, trusting one man, make the mistake of bestowing his trust on others? Did I, by casting out all fear—my own fear, and the leopard's protective fear—leave him defenceless?

Because next day, coming up the path from the stream, shouting and beating drums, were the shikaris. They had a long bamboo pole across their shoulders; and slung from the pole, feet up, head down, was the lifeless body of the leopard. It had been shot in the neck and in the head.

'We told you there was a leopard!' they shouted.

I walked home through the silent forest. It was very silent, almost as though the birds and animals knew that their trust had been violated.

I remembered the lines of a poem by D.H. Lawrence;[5] and as I climbed the steep and lonely path to my home, the words beat out their rhythm in my mind: 'There was room in the world for a mountain-lion and me.'

---

1. Sacred river of Hindustan.
2. Character in George Bernard Shaw's play Pygmalion.
3. Scottish emblem.
4. The human species.
5. English poet and novelist.

Uncommon Cold

Many years ago when I was a struggling young writer—
I am now a struggling middle-aged writer—an
English journalist of some standing asked me if I'd like to
meet Compton Mackenzie, the celebrated writer.

Mr. Mackenzie was then engaged in writing a History of
the Indian Army, a work which was to become a classic of
its kind. He was spending a few days in Calcutta, where he
was staying at the Great Eastern Hotel.

'Yes, I would like to meet him,' I said, for I had always
admired and enjoyed Mackenzie's work, particularly his
novels on the lighter side of Scottish[1] life.

Off we went to the Great Eastern, where we were
courteously received by Compton Mackenzie, who turned
out to be urbane, witty, and even rather good-looking—an
unusual combination in a successful writer! He had a short,
well-kept beard, and a mobile actor's face. I was not
surprised to learn that as a young man he had been an
actor in his father's theatrical company.

He seemed to enjoy talking to us and answering our questions, but I felt that he would have sparked even more had it not been for a heavy cold which had him sniffing and blowing his nose every now and then.

'You do have a bad cold,' I said sympathetically.

'Picked it up from Willie Maugham[2] in Bangkok[3]' he responded, 'Maugham is always catching colds and passing them on to the other people.'

'Do you mean Somerset Maugham?' I asked in a reverent tone.

'That's right. Have you met him?'

'Er—no.'

Compton Mackenzie started talking about Maugham but he was interrupted by the ringing of the telephone.

'I shall have to dash off,' he said, after taking the call. 'I'm late for an appointment.'

Reluctantly, he said goodbye.

The next morning I was sniffing. By mid-afternoon my eyes had begun to water. By evening I was sneezing with great abandon.

I was beginning to feel pretty miserable when the thought struck me: I've caught Compton Mackenzie's cold, and he got it from Somerset Maugham. The germs from two famous authors are rushing around is my system. If I can't write a decent story now, I never will!

I sat down at my typewriter and rattled off a new story.

A fortnight later I received a letter of acceptance from the editor of a popular magazine. My fist appearance in print!

Call it what you will—luck, coincidence, auto suggestion—I'm still convinced it was that uncommon cold I had caught!

---

1. Or Scotland
2. William Somerset Maugham, English novelist
3. Seaport, Thailand

Getting Rid of Guests

There is something we all want to do, although few of us will readily admit it. Get rid of our guests.

For nine months in the year only my closest friends come to see me. Then, when temperatures start soaring in the plains, long-lost acquaintances suddenly remember that I exist, and people whom I am barely able to recognise appear at the front door, willing to have me put them up for periods ranging from six days to six weeks.

This is what comes of living in a hill station. I am a forgotten man until the holidays begin. Then, suddenly, I am at the top of the popularity poll.

Occasionally I am the master of the situation. I inform the hopeful visitors that the cottage is already bursting, that people are sleeping on the floor. If the hopefuls start looking around for signs of these uncomfortable guests, I remark that they have all gone out for a picnic.

The other day I received visitors who proved to be more thick-skinned than most. The man was a friend of a friend of an acquaintance of mine. I'd never seen him before. But on the strength of this distant relationship, he'd brought his family along, together with their bedding-rolls and enough luggage for a long stay.

I tried the usual ploy but it didn't work. The man and his family were perfectly willing to share the floor-space with any others who might be staying with me.

So I made my next move. 'I must warn you about the scorpions,' I said. 'Only yesterday I found a nest of scorpions beneath the carpet.'

The scorpion-scare is effective with most people. But I was dealing with professionals. The man set his son to rolling up the carpet, saying that carpets were the reason for scorpions. The lady turned on her transistor.

'Sometimes centipedes fall from the ceiling,' I said desperately. 'And with the next shower of rain there'll be leeches crawling in at the window.'

They must have thought I was talking about the *lichis* that grow in Dehradun, because they looked quite pleased. The woman had begun to unpack. We were now interrupted by someone knocking on the front door. It was the postman, with a rejected manuscript: his arrival inspired me to greater inventiveness.

'I'm terribly sorry,' I said, staring hard at a rejection slip. 'I'm afraid I have to leave immediately for Rishikesh.[1] A paper wants me to interview the Maharishi.[2] I hope you won't mind. Would you like the name of a good hotel?'

'Oh don't worry about us,' said the woman expansively. 'We'll look after the house while you're away. It will be very hot in Rishikesh, but I suppose you have to earn a living. You must return soon. Only do let us know when you're coming!'

---

1. A religious retreat where river Ganga issues from the Himalayas .
2. Religious teacher.

Teach Me Something New Today

The youth's clothes were second-hand and ill-fitting, and he had no shoes; but there was self-confidence in his stance, and his smile was sunny. People who come from the hills are usually quick to smile.

'Can you give me a job?' he asked.

I hesitated. I was living alone more than a mile out of the hill-station of Mussoorie, and I did need someone to help me around the cottage; but I wasn't sure that I could afford the luxury of a servant.

Said the young man (he must have been about eighteen): 'I've spent all day looking for a suitable person to work for. When I saw you, I decided that no one else had a chance!'

'But can you cook?' I asked, determined not to be taken in by his bare-faced flattery.

'I can cook,' he said confidently.

Roop Singh's confidence was not quite matched by his skill. After taking him on at a modest wage, I spent a week instructing him in the mysteries of making omelettes. He was a quick learner, and was soon serving up some interesting, if not always digestible, meals. He could light a fire, which was more than an impractical writer could achieve; and he had a simple bamboo-flute which he played vigorously whenever I was at my typewriter, in spite of my assurances that it did not help in the writing of my novel.

Roop Singh had only done a year or two at school, and had started earning a living at the age of twelve. He had worked at various places—tea-shops, cycle-stands, cinemas, bus stops and railway stations—some times as a dish-washer, sometimes as a coolie. To be a full-fledged cook in a bachelor establishment (I doubt if he'd have lasted very long in any other kind of establishment) was a definite advancement—from the point of view of both salary and prestige. As soon as he received his first month's pay, he bought himself a pair of shoes, then sent the rest of the money home. 'Home' was two acres of steep, mountainside near the source of the Ganga. He had two brothers and a sister, all younger than he was, and he was anxious that they should receive the schooling he had missed.

During the afternoons, when he had finished the washing up and I had put my typewriter away, I gave him a few English lessons.

'Teach me something new today,' he would say; a request that I was to hear again and again.

Before long I had taught Roop Singh to write complete

sentences. He looked forward to our sessions under the big deodar tree on the hillside. I would stretch myself out on a carpet of pine-needles, while Roop Singh sat beside me, notebook poised, taking down my dictation in a slow, painstaking hand. Apart from writing, he loved rolling strange new words around on his tongue.

'You are very trusting with your servant,' the local grain-merchant warned me one day. 'You should lock up your house when you go out. And let the boy sleep elsewhere. Some of these boys turn out to be thieves.'

'But he's been with me a month, and I haven't lost anything!'

'Well, don't say I didn't warn you.'

Roop Singh was present when the postman brought me a money-order for two hundred rupees—a fee for a story I'd sold the previous month. It wasn't a very large amount, but it was more than Roop Singh could earn in a month. I put the money in my pocket; and at night, when I went to bed, I placed the wad of notes under my pillow. I had never been very careful with my money.

It was a wild, stormy night with scudding rain, the wind rushing up and down the chimney and rattling the window-panes. I slept fitfully and was wide awake the moment someone entered the room. I recognised Roop Singh as he stood outlined against the window, which was frequently lit up by flashes of lightning. He approached my bed, seemed to satisfy himself that I still slept, and then slipped his hand under the pillow. I lay perfectly still until he had taken the money, and even then I did not stir until he had slipped out of the front door.

Then, profoundly discouraged, and too dismayed to bother to get up and shut the door, I turned over on my side and lay awake in the dark.

The loss of the money did not trouble me very much, although I knew it would be some time before I sold another story. Undoubtedly Roop Singh's need was greater than mine. But I felt saddened and lonely, and I kept telling myself that this would never have happened if I had been a little careful and kept temptation out of his way. Finally I fell asleep.

I woke to bright sunshine and the shrieking of parrots. Roop Singh was standing beside my bed, a cup of tea in his hands, the usual smile on his face. I sat up in bed, rubbing my eyes. Had I dreamt the whole thing? Had it all been a horrible nightmare?

After Roop Singh had left the room, I put my hand under the pillow and extracted the wad of notes. They were all there, but they were still wet from the night's rain. So he had taken the money; and he had just as surely brought it back.

This incident took place two years ago, and Roop Singh is still with me. I have never spoken to him about what happened that night, or asked him why he came back. Later that same day, he came to me with his notebook and pencil, sat down beside me under the deodar, and said: 'Teach me something new today.' Perhaps that had something to do with it; and I realised that I, too, had learnt something new.

The Typewriter

Working during the long nights in an attic room provided by my aunt, I took six months to finish my first novel. I was eighteen at the time, and though the novel was about growing up in India, I was living in Jersey, in the Channel Islands, earning about £4 a week as a Public Works clerk; it was the minimum wage in the fifties. I hadn't been away from India longer than a year, but I was very homesick, and writing the book helped to take me back to the people and places I had known and loved.

Working with me in the same office was a sympathetic soul, a senior clerk whose name was Mr. Bromley. He came from Lancashire.[1] His wife and son were dead, and he lived alone in lodgings near the St. Helier sea-front. As my aunt's house was close by, I would sometimes accompany Mr. Bromley home after work, walking with him along the sea wall, watching the waves hissing along the sandy beaches or crashing against the rocks.

I gathered from some of his remarks that he was suffering from a serious illness, and that he had come to live and work in Jersey in the hope that a kinder climate would help to put him on the road to recovery or at least give him a slightly longer lease of life. He sensed that we were in a way both exiles, our real homes far from this small, rather commercialised island in the Channel. He had read widely, and sympathised with my ambitions to be a writer. He had tried it once himself, but without any success.

'I didn't have the perseverance, lad,' he said. 'I wasn't inventive enough, either. It isn't enough to be able to write well—you have to know how to tell a story.... Mr. Bromley admired my naive but determined attempt to write a book.

On a Saturday afternoon I was standing in front of a large store, gazing rather wistfully at a small. portable typewriter on display in the shop-window. It was just what I needed. My book was nearly finished but I knew I'd have to get it typed before submitting it to a publisher.

'Buying a typewriter, lad?' Mr. Bromley had stopped beside me.

'I wish I could,' I said. 'But it's £19 and I've only £6 saved up. I'll have to hire an old machine.'

'But a neat typescript can make a world of difference, lad. Editors are harassed people. If they find a dirty manuscript in front of them, they feel like chucking it in the waste-paper basket.'

'There's an old typewriter belonging to my aunt, but it should be in a museum. The letter 'b' is missing. She must have used that one a lot—or perhaps it was my uncle. Anyway, when I type my stories on it, I have to go through them afterwards and ink in all the missing 'b's.'

'That won't do, lad. Tell you what, though. Give me your £6 and I'll add £13 to it, and we'll buy the machine. Then you can pay me back out of your wages—a pound a week. Would that suit you?'

I accepted with alacrity and walked down the street in a state of euphoria, the gleaming new typewriter in my hand: I sat up late that night, hammering out the first chapter of my book.

It was mid-summer then, and by the end of the year I had paid £6 back to Mr. Bromley. It was then that I received a letter from a publisher (the third to whom I had submitted the book) saying that they liked my novel but had some suggestions to make, and could I call on them the next time I visited London? I took a few days' leave and crossed the Channel to England.

London swept me off my feet. Theatres and bookshops exerted their magic on me. And the publishers said they would take my book if only I'd try writing it again! At eighteen I was prepared to rewrite a dozen times, so I took a room in Hampstead and grabbed the first job that came my way.

For several months I was unable to send any money to Mr. Bromley. My wage was small and London was expensive. I meant to write to him, explaining the situation, but kept putting it off, telling myself that I would write as soon as I had some money to send him. I wrote my novel a third time, and it was accepted, and I received a modest advance. This time I wrote to Mr. Bromley, telling him all that had happened, and enclosing a cheque for the balance of what I still owed him.

The cheque and the letter came back in the post, along with a note from my former employer saying that Mr. Bromley had gone away and had not left a forwarding address. It seemed that he had given up his quest for better health and had decided to end his days in his own part of the country.

And so my debt was never paid. The typewriter is still with me. I have used it for over twenty-five years, and it is now old and battered. But I will not throw it away. It is like a guilty conscience, always beside me, always reminding to pay my debts in time.

The Garden of Memories

Sitting in the sun on a winter's afternoon, feeling my age just a little (I'm sixty-seven now), I began reminiscing about my boyhood in the Dehra of long ago, and I found myself missing the old times—friends of my youth, my grandmother, our neighbours, interesting characters in our small town, and, of course, my eccentric relative—the dashing young Uncle Ken!

Yes, Dehra was a small town then—uncluttered, uncrowded, with quiet lanes and pretty gardens and shady orchards.

The only time in my life that I was fortunate enough to live in a house with a real garden—as opposed to a back yard or balcony or windswept verandah—was during those three years when I spent my winter holidays (December to March) in Granny's bungalow on the Old Survey Road.

The best months were February and March, when the garden was heavy with the scent of sweet peas, the flower beds a many-coloured quilt of phlox, antirrhinum, larkspur, petunia and Californian poppy. I loved the bright yellows of the Californian poppies, the soft pinks of our own Indian poppies, the subtle perfume of petunias and snapdragons, and above all, the delicious, overpowering scent of the massed sweet peas which grew taller than me. Flowers made a sensualist of me. They taught me the delight of smell and colour and touch—yes, touch too, for to press a rose to one's lips is very like a gentle, hesitant, exploratory kiss...

Granny decided on what flowers should be sown, and where. Dhuki, the gardener, did the digging and weeding, sowing and transplanting. He was a skinny, taciturn old man, who had begun to resemble the weeds he flung away. He did not mind answering my questions, but never did he allow our brief conversations to interfere with his work. Most of the time he was to be found on his haunches, hoeing and weeding with a little spade called a *khurpi*. He would throw out the smaller marigolds because he said Granny did not care for them. I felt sorry for these colourful little discards, collected them, and transplanted them to a little garden patch of my own at the back of the house, near the garden wall.

Another so-called weed that I liked was a little purple flower that grew in clusters all over Dehra, on any bit of wasteland, in ditches, on canal banks. It flowered from late winter into early summer, and it will be growing in the valley and beyond long after gardens have become obsolete, as indeed they must, considering the rapid spread of urban clutter. It brightens up fields and roads where you least expect a little colour. I have since learnt that it is called *Ageratum,* and that it is actually prized as a garden flower in Europe, where it is described as 'Blue Mink' in the seed catalogues. Here it isn't blue but purple and it grows all the way from Rajpur (just above Dehra) to the outskirts of Meerut; then it disappears.

Other garden outcasts include the lantana bush, an attractive wayside shrub; the thorn apple, various thistles, daisies and dandelions. But both Granny and Dhuki had declared a war on weeds, and many of these commoners had to exist outside the confines of the garden. Like slum children, they survived rather well in ditches and on the roadside, while their more pampered fellow citizens were prone to leaf diseases and parasitic infections of various kinds.

The verandah was a place where Granny herself could potter about, attending to various ferns, potted palms and colourful geraniums. She averred that geraniums kept snakes away, although she never said why. As far as I know, snakes don't have a great sense of smell.

One day I saw a snake curled up at the bottom of the verandah steps. When it saw me, or became aware of my footsteps, it uncoiled itself and slithered away. I told Granny about it, and observed that it did not seem to be bothered by the geraniums.

'Ah,' said Granny. 'But for those geraniums, the snake would have entered the house!' There was no arguing with Granny.

Or with Uncle Ken, when he was at his most pontifical.

One day, while walking near the canal bank, we came upon a green grass snake holding a frog in its mouth. The frog was half in, half out, and with the help of my hockey stick, I made the snake disgorge the unfortunate creature. It hopped away, none the worse for its adventure.

I felt quite pleased with myself. 'Is this what it feels like to be God?' I mused aloud.

'No,' said Uncle Ken. 'God would have let the snake finish its lunch.'

Uncle Ken was one of those people who went through life without having to do much, although a great deal seemed to happen around him. He acted as a sort of catalyst for events that involved the family, friends, neighbours, the town itself. He believed in the fruits of hard work: other people's hard work.

Ken was good-looking as a boy, and his sisters doted on him. He took full advantage of their devotion, and, as the girls grew up and married, Ken took it for granted that they and their husbands would continue to look after his welfare. You could say he was the originator of the welfare state; his own.

I'll say this for Uncle Ken, he had a large fund of curiosity in his nature, and he loved to explore the town we lived in, and any other town or city where he might happen to find himself. With one sister settled in Lucknow, another in Ranchi, a third in Bhopal, a fourth in Pondicherry, and a fifth in Barrackpore, Uncle Ken managed to see a cross-section of India by dividing his time between all his sisters and their long-suffering husbands.

Uncle Ken liked to walk. Occasionally he borrowed my bicycle, but he had a tendency to veer off the main road and into ditches and other obstacles after a collision with a bullock cart, in which he tore his trousers and damaged the handlebar of my bicycle Uncle Ken concluded that walking was the best way of getting around Dehra.

Uncle Ken dressed quite smartly for a man of no particular occupation. He had a blue-striped blazer and a red-striped blazer; he usually wore white or off-white trousers, immaculately pressed (by Granny). He was the delight of shoeshine boys, for he was always having his shoes polished. Summers he wore a straw hat, telling everyone he had worn it for the Varsity Boat Race, while rowing for Oxford (he hadn't been to England, let alone Oxford); winters, he wore one of Grandfather's old felt hats. He seldom went bareheaded. At thirty he was almost completely bald, prompting Aunt Mabel to remark: 'Well, Ken, you must be grateful for small mercies. At least you'll never have bats getting entangled in your hair.'

Thanks to all his walking Uncle Ken had a good digestion, which kept pace with a hearty appetite. Our walks would be punctuated by short stops at *chaat* shops, sweet shops, fruit stalls, confectioners, small bakeries and other eateries.

'Have you brought any pocket money along?' he would ask, for he was usually broke.

'Granny gave me five rupees.'

'We'll try some *rasgullas*, then.'

And the rasgullas would be followed by *gulab jamuns*, until my five rupees were finished. Uncle Ken received a small allowance from Granny, but he ferreted it away to spend on clothes, preferring to spend my pocket money on perishables such as ice creams, *kulfis* and Indian sweets.

On one occasion, when neither of us had any money, Uncle Ken decided to venture into a sugarcane field on the outskirts of the town. He had broken off a stick of cane, and was busy chewing on it, when the owner of the field spotted us and let out a volley of imprecations. We fled from the field with the irate farmer giving chase. I could run faster than Uncle Ken, and did so. The farmer would have caught up with Uncle Ken if the latter's hat hadn't blown off, causing a diversion. The farmer picked up the hat, examined it, seemed to fancy it, and put it on. Several small boys clapped and cheered. The farmer marched off, wearing the hat, and Uncle Ken wisely decided against making any attempt to retrieve it.

'I'll get another one,' he said philosophically.

He wore a pith helmet, or sola *topee*, for the next few days, as he thought it would protect him from sticks and stones. For a while he harboured a paranoia that all the sugarcane farmers in the valley were looking for him, to avenge his foray into their fields. But after some time he discarded the topee because, according to him, it interfered with his good looks.

* * *

Granny grew the best sweet peas in Dehra. But she never entered them at the Annual Flower Show, held every year in the second week of March. She did not grow flowers to win prizes, she said; she grew them to please the spirit of Grandfather, who still hovered about the house and grounds he'd built thirty years earlier.

Miss Kellner, Granny's crippled but valued tenant, said the flowers were grown to attract beautiful butterflies, and she was right. In early summer, swarms of butterflies flitted about the garden.

Uncle Ken had no compunction about winning prizes, even though he did nothing to deserve them. Without telling anyone, he submitted a large display of Granny's sweet peas for the flower show, and when the prizes were announced, lo and behold! Kenneth Clerke had been awarded first prize for his magnificent display of sweet peas.

Granny refused to speak to him for several days.

Uncle Ken had been hoping for a cash prize, but they gave him a flower vase. He told me it was a Ming vase. But it looked more like Meerut to me. He offered it to Granny, hoping to propitiate her; but, still displeased with him, she gave it to Mr. Khastgir, the artist next door, who kept his paintbrushes in it.

Although I was sometimes a stubborn and unruly boy (my hero was Richmal Crompton's 'William'), I got on well with old ladies, especially those who, like Miss Kellner, were fond of offering me chocolates, marzipans, soft *nankattai* biscuits (made at Yusuf's bakery in the Dilaram Bazaar), and pieces of crystallised ginger. Miss Kellner couldn't walk—had never walked—and so she could only admire the garden from a distance, but it was from her that I learnt the names of many flowers, trees, birds and even butterflies.

Uncle Ken wasn't any good at names, but he wanted to catch a rare butterfly. He said he could make a fortune if he caught a leaf butterfly called the Purple Emperor. He equipped himself with a butterfly net, a bottle of ether, and a cabinet for mounting his trophies; he then prowled all over the grounds, making frequent forays at anything that flew. He caught several common species—Red Admirals, a Tortoiseshell, a Painted Lady, even the occasional dragonfly—but the high-flying Purple Emperor and other exotics eluded him, as did the fortune he was always aspiring to make.

Eventually he caught an angry wasp, which stung him through the netting. Chased by its fellow wasps, he took refuge in the lily pond and emerged sometime later draped in lilies and water weeds.

After this, Uncle Ken retired from the butterfly business, insisting that tiger-hunting was safer.

Remember this Day

If you can get an entire year off from school when you are nine years old, and can have a memorable time with a great father, then that year has to be the best time of your life even if it is followed by sorrow and insecurity.

It was the result of my parents' separation at a time when my father was on active service in the R.A.F. during World War II. He managed to keep me with him for a summer and winter, at various locations in New Delhi—Hailey Road, Atul Grove Lane, Scindia House—in apartments he had rented, as he was not permitted to keep a child in the quarters assigned to service personnel. This arrangement suited me perfectly, and I had a wonderful year in Delhi, going to the cinema, quaffing milkshakes, helping my father with his stamp collection; but this idyllic situation could not continue for ever, and when my father was transferred to Karachi he had no option but to put me in a boarding school.

This was the Bishop Cotton Preparatory School in Simla—or rather, Chhota Simla—where boys studied up to Class 4, after which they moved on to the senior school.

Although I was a shy boy, I had settled down quite well in the friendly atmosphere of this little school, but I did miss my fathers' companionship, and I was overjoyed when he came up to see me during the midsummer break. He had a couple of days' leave, and he could only take me out for a day, bringing me back to school in the evening.

I was so proud of him when he turned up in his dark blue R.A.F. uniform, a Flight Lieutenant's stripes very much in evidence as he had just been promoted. He was already forty, engaged in Codes and Ciphers and not flying much. He was short and stocky, getting bald, but smart in his uniform. I gave him a salute—I loved giving salutes—and he returned the salutation and followed it up with a hug and a kiss on my forehead.

'And what would you like to do today, son?'

'Let's go to Davico's,' I said.

Davico's was the best restaurant in town, famous for its meringues, marzipans, curry-puffs and pastries.

So to Davico's we went, where of course I gorged myself on confectionery as only a small schoolboy can do.

'Lunch is still a long way off, so let's take a walk,' suggested my father. And provisioning ourselves with more pastries, we left the Mall and trudged up to the Monkey Temple at the top of Jakko Hill. Here we were relieved of the pastries by the monkeys, who simply snatched them away from my unwilling hands, and we came downhill in a hurry before I could get hungry again. Small boys and monkeys have much in common.

My father suggested a rickshaw ride around Elysium Hill, and this we did in style, swept along by four sturdy young rickshaw-pullers. My father took the opportunity of relating the story of Kipling's *Phantom Rickshaw* (this was before I discovered it in print), and a couple of other ghost stories designed to build up my appetite for lunch.

We ate at Wenger's (or was it Clark's?) and then—

'Enough of ghosts, Ruskin. Let's go to the pictures.'

I loved going to the pictures. I know the Delhi cinemas intimately, and it hadn't taken me long to discover the Simla cinemas. There were three of them—the Regal, the Ritz, and the Rivoli.

We went to the Rivoli. It was down near the ice-skating ring and the old Blessington Hotel. The film was about an ice-skater and starred Sonja Henie, a pretty young Norwegian Olympic champion who appeared in a number of Hollywood musicals. All she had to do was skate and look pretty, and this she did to perfection. I decided to fall in love with her. But by the time I'd grow up and finished school, she'd stopped skating and making films! Whatever happened to Sonja Henie?

After the picture it was time to return to school. We walked all the way to Chhota Simla, talking about what we'd do during the winter holidays, and where we would go when the War was over.

'I'll be in Calcutta now,' said my father. 'There are good bookshops there. And cinemas. And Chinese restaurants. And we'll buy more gramophone records, and add to the stamp collection.'

It was dusk when we walked slowly down the path to the school gate and playing-field. Two of my friends were waiting for me—Bimal and Riaz. My father spoke to them, asked about their homes. A bell started ringing. We said goodbye.

'Remember this day, Ruskin,' said my father.

He patted me gently on the head and walked away.

I never saw him again.

Three months later I heard that he had passed away in the military hospital in Calcutta.

I dream of him sometimes, and in my dream he is always the same, caring for me and leading me by the hand along old familiar roads.

And of course I remember that day. Over sixty-five years have passed, but it's as fresh as yesterday.

RUSKIN BOND
has also written

NOVELS

- The Room of the Roof
- Vagrants in the Valley
- A Flight of Pigeons
- The Sensualist
- A Handful of Nuts
- Maharani

STORY COLLECTIONS

- The Night Train at Deoli
- Time Stops at Shamli
- Our Trees Still Grow in Dehra
- When Darkness Falls
- A Season of Ghosts
- Dust on the Mountain: Collected Stories
- Secrets
- A Face in the Dark

NON-FICTION

- Scenes from a Writer's Life
- The Lamp Is Lit
- Notes From A Small Room
- Book of Nature
- Book of Humour
- Rain in the Mountains
- Landour Days
- The India I Love
- A Town Called Dehra
- Roads to Mussoorie
- A Little Book of Life

POETRY

- Book of Verse
- Hip-Hop Nature Boy
- A Little Night Music

FOR YOUNG READERS

- Crazy Times with Uncle Ken
- Mr. Oliver's Diary
- Escape From Java
- The Hidden Pool
- The Parrot Who Wouldn't Talk
- The Kashmiri Story-teller
- Treasury of Children's Stories
- Adventures of Rusty (series of 5)
- The Cherry Tree
- Getting Granny's Glasses
- The Blue Umbrella
- Angry River
- Road to the Bazaar
- Too Much Trouble
- Romi and the Wildfire
- Tiger my Friend
- Great Stories for Children
- Children's Omnibus
- Tigers for Dinner
- At School with Ruskin
- A Bond With Nature
- Friends in Small Places
- Tales of the Open Road

All the above titles are available at NATRAJ: The Green Bookshop, Dehra Dun

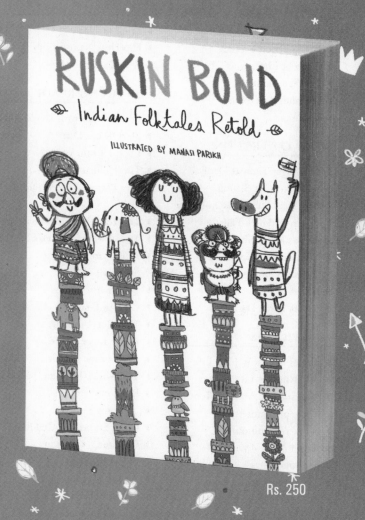

RUSKIN BOND
☙ Indian Folktales Retold ☙

ILLUSTRATED BY MANASI PARIKH

Rs. 250

IN THIS COLLECTION OF SHORT STORIES, INDIA'S FAVOURITE
STORYTELLER RETELLS INDIA'S FORGOTTEN FOLKTALES.

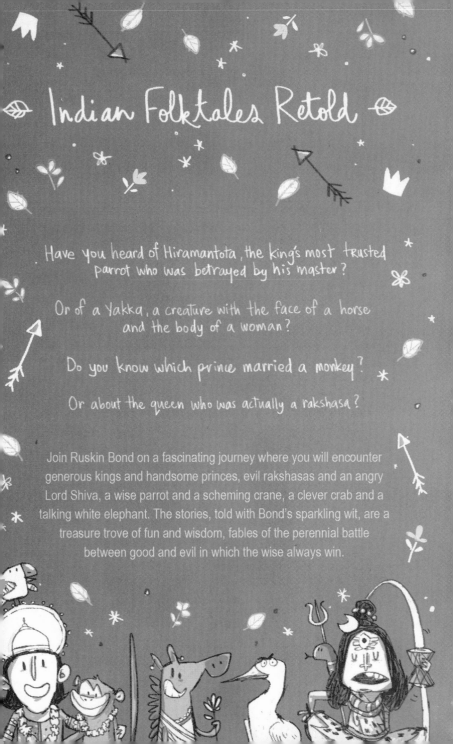

Indian Folktales Retold

Have you heard of Hiramantota, the king's most trusted parrot who was betrayed by his master?

Or of a Yakka, a creature with the face of a horse and the body of a woman?

Do you know which prince married a monkey?

Or about the queen who was actually a rakshasa?

Join Ruskin Bond on a fascinating journey where you will encounter generous kings and handsome princes, evil rakshasas and an angry Lord Shiva, a wise parrot and a scheming crane, a clever crab and a talking white elephant. The stories, told with Bond's sparkling wit, are a treasure trove of fun and wisdom, fables of the perennial battle between good and evil in which the wise always win.